THE
ULTIMATE
JEWISH
TRIVIA BOOK

500 Questions
to Test Your **Oy Q**

Signe Bergstrom

FALL RIVER PRESS

New York

FALL RIVER PRESS

New York

An Imprint of Sterling Publishing
387 Park Avenue South
New York, NY 10016

FALL RIVER PRESS and the distinctive Fall River Press logo
are registered trademarks of Barnes & Noble, Inc.

ISBN: 978-1-4351-2741-8

Printed and bound in the United States of America

1 3 5 7 9 10 8 6 4 2

The information in this book has been drawn from many sources
and is assumed to be accurate. Although every effort has been made to verify
the information, the publishers cannot guarantee its perfect accuracy.

contents

The Whole Megillah

Ponder this: approximately 22 percent of Nobel Prize winners have been Jews, despite the fact that Jews comprise less than one-quarter of 1 percent of the world's population. Choose any field—science, economics, entertainment, medicine—and you'll find not one, not two, but a long list of Jews who have excelled in it. Even sports—yes, sports. (Heard of Sandy Koufax? No? Turn to page 58.) And don't get me started on the field of psychotherapy; we practically invented it. Oy vey.

Yes, we've spent years and years being among the persecuted; in some neighborhoods and corners of the earth, we still are. But, through all the tears, anger, and hostility, we've emerged with a fail-proof weapon: laughter. If you don't start laughing, you'll never stop crying. Laughter is a form of resiliency, after all. Beyond this, though, we also happen to be really smart. Don't believe me? Three words: Marx, Freud, and Einstein. Now that's what I call an impressive resume.

So, if we're so smart, why don't we know more about who we are and where we're from?

The Ultimate Jewish Trivia Book is the perfect way to exercise your noggin. Chock-full of interesting and often little-known factoids, it's a guidebook for every Jew, whether wise or simple. Covering information on everything from Biblical history to the wonderful world of fashion, *The Ultimate Jewish Trivia Book* delves into the whole megillah...and then some.

CHAPTER ONE

The Good Old Days: Jewish and Israeli History

> "[God,] I know we are your chosen people, but once in
> a while, can't you choose someone else?"
> —Tevye in *Fiddler on the Roof*

Mel Brook's classic 1981 film, *History of the World, Part One*, spans the great swath of time, with Brooks appearing in no fewer than five roles, Moses and Comicus, the stand-up philosopher, among them. From the Dawn of Man to the French Revolution, the film includes re-enactments of the giving of the Ten Commandments and the Last Supper. And so it is with this chapter: to recount the history of the Jew and his impact on civilization, one would have to cast the lens far into the past; Judaism is one of the world's few cultures that seems to have seen it all. Been there. Done that. Before the New Testament, there was the Old. Before the civil calendar, there was the lunisolar calendar, with all its million and one Jewish holidays. And while we pride ourselves on the longevity of our culture, for the sake of brevity, we've cut to the chase to give you the ultimate questions that test the core of who you are and where you came from. Descendant of Moses? Sure. Descendant of Abraham? Maybe. Descendant of Esau? Who? Gotcha.

1. **About 3,800 years ago, what did Terah, along with his son Abraham, Abraham's wife Sarah, and his grandson Lot, do, to be considered *Ivri* (Hebrew)?**

   a. He changed his son's name from Abram to Abraham
   b. He built an altar
   c. He tended a flock of sheep
   d. He fled the City of Ur and crossed the River Eber

2. **What did Abraham establish regarding the land of Haran (located in modern day Turkey), that would forever affect the identity of many of his descendants?**

   a. A synagogue
   b. A covenant with God
   c. A woodsmith shop
   d. A dried goods store

3. **Which of Abraham's sons became the father of the Arab nation?**

   a. Ishmael
   b. Isaac
   c. Abimelech
   d. Zimran

4. **Which of Abraham's grandsons would reject the covenant?**

   a. Esau
   b. Ishbak
   c. Midian
   d. Jokshan

5. Jacob, another of Abraham's grandsons, confirmed the covenant. For this, what did God change his name to?

a. Joshua
b. Ishmael
c. Israel
d. Nahor

6. What are Jacob's twelve children known as?

a. The Chosen
b. The Tribe of Judah
c. The Many
d. The Israelites

7. Whom is a Jew a descendant of?

a. Judah
b. Yahweh
c. Abraham
d. Saul

8. Who was David Ben-Gurion?

a. A leader of civil rights
b. The first prime minister of Israel
c. The first king of Israel
d. The last son of Abraham

9. Who is an Israeli?

a. Any Jewish person
b. Anyone who declares himself so
c. Someone who is born and/or lives in Israel
d. Someone who believes in God

Anne Frank

✡

"I don't think of all the misery but of the beauty that still remains." —Anne Frank

Since its original publication in 1947, Anne Frank's *Diary of a Young Girl* remains one of the most moving testaments to the tragedy of the Holocaust. Written over the course of two years while hiding from the Nazis with her family and friends inside an Amsterdam warehouse, Frank's diary provides an intimate glimpse inside the mind of a teenage girl. It rages with emotions typical of adolescence but also offers words of hope and innocence during a dark time in history. Anne died in the Bergen-Belsen concentration camp just three months shy of her sixteenth birthday. Her unwavering belief that good would triumph over evil remains an inspiring example of the depth and strength of the human spirit when faced with adversity and madness.

10. **What is the land of milk and honey also called?**

    a. Greece

    b. Tel Aviv

    c. The Promised Land

    d. Heaven

11. Outside of Israel, which country has the largest Jewish population?

a. France
b. Russia
c. Ukraine
d. The United States

12. The name Adam comes from the Hebrew word *Adamah*, which means what?

a. The first
b. Ground, or earth
c. Friend
d. Light

13. Who was Abraham Isaac Kook?

a. The first chief rabbi of Israel
b. The first prime minister of Israel
c. A famous historian
d. Founder of the Delos Synagogue

14. What are *teraphim*?

a. Protective spirits
b. A sect of Judaism
c. Statues of local deities
d. A group of artisans

15. According to the Jewish calendar, which is based on a lunisolar system, what year was Abraham born?

a. 1901
b. 2000
c. 1947
d. 1948

16. In modern times, what year did Jews come back to Israel and found their nation?

   a. 1948
   b. 1959
   c. 1901
   d. 2001

17. Contrary to the concept of idolatry, what did Abraham discover?

   a. Atheism
   b. Monotheism
   c. Deism
   d. Pantheism

18. Instead of offering his son Isaac to God, what did Abraham sacrifice instead?

   a. A goat
   b. A ram
   c. Himself
   d. His wife

19. According to tradition, which four couples are buried in the Cave of the Patriarchs in Hebron?

   a. Adam and Eve, Isaac and Sarah, Jacob and Leah, Abraham and Rebekah
   b. Adam and Eve, Abraham and Sarah, Isaac and Leah, Jacob and Rebekah
   c. Adam and Eve, Abraham and Leah, Isaac and Sarah, Jacob and Rebekah
   d. Adam and Eve, Abraham and Sarah, Isaac and Rebekah, and Jacob and Leah

20. According to tradition, why is Rachel, Jacob's other wife, buried in a tomb of her own?

    a. Since she died giving birth, she has a tomb of her own so she can pray for her children as they pass her on their way to exile
    b. She died alone and, therefore, was buried alone
    c. Her family couldn't afford to bury her with them
    d. She requested to be buried alone

21. Who was the first person to use the name "Tel Aviv," which later became the name for the first modern city in Israel?

    a. Joshua
    b. Chaim Nachman Bialik
    c. Nahum Sokolow
    d. David Ben-Gurion

22. What did Moses bring to the Jewish people from the top of Mount Sinai?

    a. The Ten Commandments
    b. The Holy Ark
    c. The Torah
    d. Prayer shawls

23. Which artist was commissioned in 1505 by Pope Julius II to carve a statue of Moses?

    a. Cellini
    b. Michelangelo
    c. Donatello
    d. Verrocchio

24. Complete the title of Sigmund Freud's famous book: *Moses and…*

a. *God*
b. *the Mountain*
c. *the Id*
d. *Monotheism*

25. What is the Hebrew meaning of "Moses"?

a. Water
b. Reeds
c. Gifted
d. Drawn (drawn out)

26. Moses is famous for saying which of the following quotes?

a. "As a man thinks in his heart, so is he."
b. "At the touch of love, everyone becomes a poet."
c. "Let my people go."
d. "Let him who is without sin cast the first stone."

27. What were the ten plagues God set forth on the Egyptians as a prelude to the Jewish exodus?

a. Blood, frogs, lice, wild animals, plague, boils, hail, locusts, darkness, and death of the firstborn
b. Blood, mice, lice, wild animals, hail, boils, sandstorm, locusts, darkness, and death of the firstborn
c. Blood, frogs, heat, wild animals, plague, disease, hail, locusts, darkness, and death of the firstborn
d. Blood, frogs, leprosy, wild animals, plague, boils, hail, locusts, darkness, and death of the firstborn

28. Where is Mount Sinai?

a. Its exact location is unknown
b. Egypt
c. Israel
d. Ukraine

29. What is the First Commandment?

a. "Thou shalt have no other gods before me."
b. "I am the Lord thy God."
c. "You shall not make for yourself an idol..."
d. "Remember the Sabbath day, and to keep it holy."

30. What do the first five commandments define?

a. How to live
b. Proper etiquette
c. A person's relationship to morality
d. A person's duties regarding his relationship to God

31. What do the second set of Commandments define?

a. The relationship of man to his fellow man
b. How to work
c. A person's relationship to morality
d. A code of living

32. How many laws does the Torah detail?

a. 63
b. 600
c. 613
d. 16

33. Complete the following statement from Hillel the Elder: "If I am not for myself...

a. ...who will head the call?"
b. ...who will find the way?"
c. ...who will be for me?"
d. ...who will rise up and fight?"

34. How long did the Jews wander in the wilderness from Egypt to Canaan?

a. 40 years
b. 400 years
c. 4 years
d. 44 years

35. When toasting someone for a long life, it's popular to say, "May you live to 120." What is significant about this number?

a. It represents the number of people who gathered around Moses at Mount Sinai
b. It's simply a superstitious number that represents good luck
c. It represents the number of followers who first converted to Judaism
d. Moses lived to that age

36. According to tradition, what frightened the inhabitants of Jericho?

a. The impending darkness
b. A plague of locusts
c. The sound of the *shofar*, the ram's horn
d. Nothing

37. How did the Jews divide the Holy Land fairly among twelve different tribes?

a. They held a lottery
b. They divided the land into twelve equal plots
c. The land was divided according to rank
d. They held a contest

38. Who is popularly referred to as the Jewish Joan of Arc?

a. Deborah
b. Esther
c. Abigail
d. Miriam

39. Samson can be considered which of the following:

a. A *langer lucksh*
b. A *shtarker*
c. A *nishtikeit*
d. An *Apikoros*

40. What weapon did Samson use to slay an entire army of Philistines?

a. A slingshot
b. A sword
c. His hair
d. A donkey's jawbone

41. What happened to Samson when Delilah had his hair cut while he slept?

   a. He lost his power, was blinded by the Philistines, then was taken prisoner

   b. He lost his power and was banished from the village

   c. He lost his power and was forced to walk through the village in shame

   d. He lost his power and lived the rest of his life in a cave

42. What were Samson's last words?

   a. "May the pillars destroy us all!"

   b. "Do not forsake me!"

   c. "I loved not."

   d. "Let me die with the Philistines!"

43. Who brought the Ark containing the Ten Commandments to Jerusalem and dedicated a place for a national House of God?

   a. David

   b. Joshua

   c. Abraham

   d. Isaac

44. Whom did King David seduce?

   a. Delilah

   b. Esther

   c. Bathsheba

   d. Rebekah

45. How did King David's son, Absalom, die?

    a. The king sacrificed him

    b. The Philistine army killed him

    c. His hair became entangled in the branches of a tree, leaving him hanging there to be stabbed to death

    d. He threw himself off a cliff

46. Where is Absalom's tomb located?

    a. In the valley of Kidron

    b. At the bottom of Mount Sinai

    c. He has no tomb

    d. Under a Weeping Willow tree on the outskirts of Tel Aviv

47. What was unique about the *menorah* in the Temple?

    a. It was made of wood

    b. It was proportionally scaled three times larger than a standard *menorah*

    c. It was made of glass

    d. It had only seven branches

48. What was the most holy area inside the Temple called?

    a. Sacred Site

    b. Circle of Holy

    c. Holy of Holies

    d. The Trident

49. What type of stone was used to build the Wailing Wall in Jerusalem?

    a. Limestone

    b. Granite

    c. Marble

    d. Sandstone

50. Who defeated the kingdom of Israel in 722 BCE?

a. Assyria

b. Egypt

c. Saudia Arabia

d. Jordan

51. Who was King Ahab married to?

a. Abigail

b. Baara

c. Sarah

d. Jezebel

52. What did King Ahab build—under his wife's influence?

a. A synagogue

b. A village

c. A pagan temple

d. A concert hall

53. Who stood up to King Ahab and Jezebel?

a. Elijah

b. Hannah

c. King Hezekiah

d. Samson

54. Who destroyed the First Temple?

a. The Babylonians

b. The Assyrians

c. The Canaanites

d. The Egyptians

55. What is the most common Yiddish word for a synogogue?

    a. *Olam*
    b. *Shul*
    c. *Rav*
    d. *Shamos*

56. What does *kohen* mean?

    a. Ambassador
    b. Leader
    c. Priest
    d. King

57. Arthur Loomis Harmon, who helped design the Empire State Building, designed what building in Jerusalem?

    a. The King David Hotel
    b. The Knesset
    c. The YMCA
    d. The Water Clock Tower Hotel

58. How many *megillot* (scrolls) are in the Bible?

    a. 35
    b. 2
    c. 10
    d. 5

59. Besides being born, what monumental event happened to Moses on his birthday?

    a. He died, 120 years later
    b. His wife gave birth to his son, 40 years later
    c. He was married, 18 years later
    d. He climbed Mount Sinai, 50 years later

60. According to the Jewish calendar, how are days named?

a. By number
b. By the moon and sun cycles
c. By planting and harvesting cycles
d. By astronomical numbers

61. Which city is the largest on the Sharon plain?

a. Herzliya
b. Bat Yam
c. Netanya
d. Tel-Aviv

62. What is Israel's Highway 6 also known as?

a. The Arava Road
b. The Coastal Road
c. The Trans-Israel Highway
d. Ashdod Highway

63. What is one of the most visited sites in the south of Israel?

a. Masada
b. Akko
c. Haifa
d. Bible Lands Museum

64. Which kibbutz was set up by Holocaust survivors in remembrance of its martyrs?

a. Kibbutz *Be'eri*
b. Kibbutz *Cabri*
c. Kibbutz *Lotan*
d. Kibbutz *Lohamei Hageta'ot*

65. What is a kibbutz?

    a. A type of museum
    b. A collective community in Israel
    c. A memorial
    d. A charity organization

66. Until approximately 1830, which city had the highest Jewish population in North America?

    a. New York, N.Y.
    b. Baltimore, Md.
    c. Charleston, S.C.
    d. Miami, Fla.

67. What year did the Six Day War take place, in which Israel fought the neighboring states of Egypt, Jordan, and Syria?

    a. 1967
    b. 1988
    c. 1965
    d. 1867

68. According to a CNN poll, what approximate percentage of Jews voted for Barack Obama in the 2008 presidential election?

    a. 20%
    b. 50%
    c. 80%
    d. 10%

69. In November 2008, Eric Cantor was the first Jewish Republican to be selected for what government position?

a. Presidential speechwriter
b. Chief of staff
c. House minority whip
d. Minority leader

70. According to most historians, who was the first Jew to set foot in the New World?

a. Christopher Columbus's interpreter
b. Levi Strauss
c. John Alden's nanny
d. Giovanni de Verrazzano's assistant

71. What do Judith Resnick, Scott Horowitz, Jeffrey Hoffman, and David Wolf have in common?

a. They are all U.S. senators
b. They were all member of the first group of Jews in New Amsterdam
c. They are all astronauts
d. Nothing

72. What incident led to the formation of the Anti-Defamation League?

a. The lynching of Leo Frank
b. The bombing of a synagogue in Charleston, S.C.
c. Martin Luther King Jr.'s death
d. The publication of *The Protocols of the Elders of Zion*

73. When did Operation Moses take place?

  a. 1964
  b. 1972
  c. 1980
  d. 1984

74. What did this covert operation entail?

  a. The journey of 8,000 Ethiopian Jews through Sudan to Israel
  b. The establishment of a Jewish "State" of Ararat on Grand Island near Niagara Falls
  c. The establishment of the first Jewish-American ghetto
  d. The removal of 60 Jews from Hebron during an Arab riot

75. What were the Spanish Jews who chose conversion in 1392–1492 and continued to practice Judaism called?

  a. Kabbalists
  b. Marranos
  c. Pietists
  d. Sephardim

CHAPTER TWO

L'Chaim: Holidays

"Most Texans think *Hanukkah* is some kind of duck call."
—comedian Richard Lewis

Autumn's Jewish holidays occur in such rapid succession—and fall on different dates on the Gregorian calendar every year—that one could suspect the rabbis of inventing them just to score extra bonus points. Yes, there are a ton of Jewish holidays, and even the uber-faithful sometimes get them mixed up. Sukkot? Real or imaginary? Cholent? A type of festival, a stew, or both? (See page 77, question 16 for the answer.) When in doubt, simply hoist your glass and give a hearty "*L'Chaim*"… and call your mother. But you already do that every day, don't you?

1. According to the Jewish calendar, when is *Purim* celebrated?

    a. On the tenth day of *Tishrei*

    b. On the first day of *Tishrei*

    c. On the fourteenth day of *Adar*

    d. One the fifteenth day of *Nisan*

2. Which *megillah* (scroll) is read during *Purim*?

    a. Lametations

    b. Book of Ruth

    c. Song of Songs

    d. Book of Esther

3. Which of the following is *not* a *mitzvah* during *Purim*?

    a. Listening to a public *megillah* reading

    b. Dancing with friends

    c. Sending food gifts

    d. Eating a festive meal

4. In eighteenth-century Romania, *Purim* became known for its satirical performances with song and dance. What were these performances a precursor to?

    a. Yiddish theater

    b. Vaudeville

    c. Line dancing

    d. Puppetry

5. During *Purim* in Italy, what do children traditionally pelt each other with?

    a. Nuts

    b. Oranges

    c. Eggs

    d. Cookies

6. What beverage is traditionally part of *Purim* dinner?

    a. Soda
    b. Salt water
    c. Apple juice
    d. Wine

7. Which is a traditional food eaten during *Purim*?

    a. *Charoses*
    b. *Latkes*
    c. *Hamantaschen*
    d. *Karpas*

8. What did Esther hide from Ahasuerus?

    a. Her Jewish identity
    b. Her hair
    c. Her shawl
    d. Her smile

9. If all the non-working holidays fall on weekdays, how many days would an observant Jew need to take off from work to observe all of them?

    a. 23
    b. 10
    c. 11
    d. 13

10. Which Jewish holiday sometimes overlaps with Easter?

    a. Passover
    b. *Purim*
    c. *Yom Kippur*
    d. *Rosh Hashanah*

11. What does Passover specifically refer to?

a. The fact that God "passed over" the houses of the Jews when He was slaying the firstborn of Egypt
b. The Exodus
c. The day that the Israelites received the Ten Commandments
d. The fact that jews "pass over" the eating of bread during the holiday

12. Traditionally, what *cannot* be eaten during Passover?

a. Oranges
b. Honey
c. Oily food
d. Leavened bread

13. During Passover, what do parents hide for the children to find?

a. Gelt
b. The *afikomen*
c. A *dreidel*
d. A horn

14. Who renounced idolatry upon hearing the Torah at Sinai during the first *Shavuot*?

a. Kaleb (Caleb)
b. Jethro (Yitro)
c. Aaron (Aharon)
d. Bezeniel (Bezanial)

15. What does the name of the Jewish holiday *Shavuot* mean?

a. Weeks
b. Exodus
c. Revolt
d. Obligations

16. How long does Passover last?

    a. 3 days; 2 days outside of Israel
    b. 5 days; 6 days outside of Israel
    c. 7 days; 8 days outside of Israel
    d. 10 days

17. Which of the following is *not* an ingredient for *charoset*?

    a. Caramel
    b. Sweet wine
    c. Apples
    d. Nuts

18. What is "*Mah Nishtanah*"?

    a. A sad song sung during *Purim*
    b. A famous *Hanukkah* poem
    c. A scroll
    d. A song sung during Passover

19. What is *Kol Nidre*?

    a. The traditional prayer of Passover
    b. The holiest city in Israel
    c. The declaration at the beginning of the evening service on *Yom Kippur*
    d. The official name of the rabbi who presides over *Yom Kippur* services

20. How many hours are Jews traditionally asked to fast in observance of *Yom Kippur*?

    a. 25 hours
    b. 4 hours
    c. 8 hours
    d. 48 hours

21. A strict day of rest and atonement, which of the following is *not* a traditional prohibition during *Yom Kippur*?

a. No laughing or crying
b. No wearing of leather shoes
c. No dealing with money
d. No anointing oneself with perfumes

22. What do the eight branches of the *Hanukkah menorah* symbolize?

a. Abraham's eight sons
b. The first eight tenets of the commandments
c. The miraculous burning of oil for eight days
d. Nothing

23. Complete the sentence. *Hanukkah* is also known as the festival of...

a. Hope
b. Lights
c. Oil
d. Joy

24. What king persecuted the Jews, but thereby allowed the miracle of *Hanukkah* to occur when the Maccabees rebelled?

a. Attalus
b. Seleucus
c. Alexander the Great
d. Antiochus

25. Who lit the first *Hanukkah menorah*?

    a. A little boy

    b. The Assyrians

    c. Moses

    d. The Maccabees

26. Traditionally, what type of food is eaten on *Hanukkah*?

    a. Oily (fried) food

    b. Sweet food

    c. Salty food

    d. Fruit

27. What is *gelt*?

    a. A type of rabbinical shawl

    b. The fringes of a shawl

    c. Small amounts of money

    d. Slang for something delicious

28. What is a *dreidel*?

    a. A happy child

    b. An old-fashioned drink

    c. A type of knish

    d. A spinning top

29. Which of the following words does *not* correspond to the letters on the *dreidel*?

    a. Some

    b. Nothing

    c. All

    d. Half

30. **"Head of the year" is the literal translation of which Jewish holiday?**

a. *Pesach*
b. *Purim*
c. *Rosh Hashanah*
d. *Hanukkah*

31. **Which statement is true about *Shavuot*?**

a. On *Shavuot*, Jews read a Torah portion that includes the Ten Commandments
b. On *Shavuot*, Jews read a Torah portion about the Ten Plagues
c. On *Shavuot*, Jews read a Torah portion about crossing the Red Sea
d. On *Shavuot*, Jews read about Judah Maccabee and his brothers

32. **During *Rosh Hashanah*, it is common to eat apples dipped in what?**

a. Wine
b. Honey
c. A mixture of walnut and syrup
d. Caramel

33. **What is the common greeting during *Rosh Hashanah*?**

a. "And many more!"
b. "In health and good luck!"
c. "For a good year!"
d. "Be at ease!"

34. When do the Days of Awe take place?

a. During the first 2 days of *Purim*

b. During the last 5 days of December

c. During the 10 days from the beginning of *Rosh Hashanah* to the end of *Yom Kippur*

d. During the month of *Adar*

35. What is the Festival of Booths called in Hebrew?

a. *Tu B'Shevat*

b. *Shavuot*

c. *Tzom Gedaliah*

d. *Sukkot*

36. During *Tu B'Shevat*, what do observant Jews count?

a. The age of a recently planted tree

b. Their blessings

c. The amount almonds a tree yields

d. Everything that they are grateful for

37. There are two main symbols of *Sukkot*. One is the *etrog* (citron). What is the other?

a. The almond

b. Rain

c. Branches of trees

d. Bread

38. During *Sukkot*, observant Jews welcome *ushpizin*. What are *ushpizin*?

a. Guests

b. Messages of good cheer

c. Strangers

d. Children

Something Sweet

On the Jewish New Year, *Rosh Hashanah*, food is typically sweet. The sweetness represents the promise of good things to come in the following year. The most traditional sweet dishes typically involve honey and apples. This recipe for apples baked in honey and cider, provided by my stepmother, is a delicious and no-fuss way to bring in the cheer without having to do any heavy lifting. Now, that's what I call sweet!

Sweet and Simple Apple and Honey Recipe

Preparation time: 20 minutes   **Yield:** 4 servings
Cooking time: 50 minutes

> 2 c fresh apple cider
> 1/2 c honey
> 4 tbsp sweet butter
> Generous pinch grated nutmeg
> 4 large baking apples
> 1 c heavy cream, lightly whipped (optional)

1. Preheat oven to 400 degrees.

2. Boil the cider until it is reduced by half, about 10 minutes. Stir in the honey, butter, and nutmeg, stirring until the butter melts.

3. Core the apples, leaving the bottoms intact and peeling them two-thirds of the way down. Arrange them in a small baking dish.

4. Spoon about 2 tablespoons of the cider mixture into the center of each apple. Pour the rest of the cider over and around the apples. Bake until the apples are tender but still hold their shape, about 40 minutes. Baste several times during baking.

5. Serve warm or at room temperature, with lightly whipped cream on the side if desired.

39. Which of the following customs is *not* a custom during *Rosh Hashanah*?

a. Dipping an apple into honey
b. *Tashlikh*
c. Dipping *challah* into honey
d. Dipping eggs into salt water

40. What is the final prayer of *Yom Kippur*?

a. *Neilah*
b. *Amidah*
c. *Kaddish*
d. *Hallel*

41. Complete the phrase: "More than the Jews have kept the Sabbath…"

a. …the Jews have kept each other."
b. …the Sabbath has kept the Jews."
c. …the Sabbath has preserved us whole."
d. …the Jews are the Sabbath."

42. What is the time frame of the Sabbath?

a. From sunrise Friday until sunrise on Saturday
b. From sunrise Friday until sundown on Sunday
c. From sundown Friday until sundown on Sunday
d. From sundown Friday until sundown on Saturday

43. Where is the only place that the Sabbath is mentioned in the *Tanakh* (Bible)?

a. The Ten Commandments
b. Psalms
c. Gospels
d. Nowhere

44. What ceremony marks the beginning of the Sabbath?

a. Eating of *challah*
b. Lighting of the candles
c. Pouring of the wine
d. Reading of the Torah

45. Where does the world's largest Passover *Seder* take place?

a. France
b. Israel
c. Nepal
d. United States

46. What U.S. President was assassinated during Passover?

a. John F. Kennedy
b. Abraham Lincoln
c. James A. Garfield
d. William McKinley

47. When was the first American edition of the *Haggadah* published?

a. 1937
b. 1852
c. 1960
d. 1837

48. Which of the following should *not* be on the Seder plate?

a. Parsley
b. *Charoset*
c. Chocolate
d. Egg

49. **What is Major League Dreidel?**

    a. A betting game developed by Columbia University professors in the 1950s and played during *Hanukkah*

    b. A type of chess move

    c. The name of the company that manufactures 90 percent of the *dreidels* in the U.S.

    d. A New York-based association of hardcore *dreidel* enthusiasts

50. **What is the culinary mainstay of *Hanukkah*?**

    a. *Challah*

    b. Chicken feet

    c. *Latkes*

    d. *Matzah*

CHAPTER THREE

And All That Jazz: Entertainment

"I arrived in Hollywood without having my nose fixed, my teeth capped, or my name changed. That is very gratifying to me." —Barbra Streisand

"Let me entertain you." While those words may have been popularized by Miss Gypsy Rose Lee in Stephen Sondheim's musical, *Gypsy*, Jews have been uttering the sentence for centuries. We have top contenders and players in just about every industry, but our stars seem to shine brightest on the Great White Way and the silver screen. What can I say? We're just natural-born entertainers. Perhaps it's our impeccable sense of comedic timing or—if you'd prefer to take the psychoanalytic route—our ability to use charm as an assimilation tactic. The truth is, our culture has long depended on storytelling to recount both the written and the oral history of our people. Whether we're debating religious ideas into the wee hours on Passover, holding court over political discussion, or simply recounting what we did over the weekend, we will happily transform the mundane into a show-stopper. What's life without a good story?

1. Which entertainer has won an Academy Award, an Emmy Award, a Grammy Award, a Tony Award *and* the Pulitzer Prize?

    a. Mike Nichols
    b. Steven Spielberg
    c. Mel Brooks
    d. Marvin Hamlisch

2. Leonard Cohen's poem "Prayer for Sunset" compares the setting sun to what?

    a. An orange
    b. A Menorah
    c. The raving Absalom
    d. Death

3. Who wrote "God Bless America"?

    a. Irving Berlin
    b. Walter Damrosch
    c. Oscar Hammerstein
    d. Erich Leinsdorf

4. Carl Laemmle, born in a small village in Germany, emigrated to America and later founded what company?

    a. Universal Pictures
    b. 20th Century-Fox
    c. Warner Bros.
    d. Paramount Pictures

5. Adolph Zucker, born in Hungary, emigrated to America and later started what company?

    a. Warner Bros.
    b. Columbia Pictures
    c. Paramount Pictures
    d. RKO Radio Pictures

6. William Fox, also born in Hungary, came to American and grew up to create what company?

    a. Metro-Goldwyn-Mayer
    b. Sony Pictures
    c. Walt Disney Pictures
    d. Fox Film Corporation

7. Louis B. Mayer, born in Russia, emigrated to Canada, later moved to Boston, and eventually headed what company?

    a. New Line Cinema
    b. Castle Rock Entertainment
    c. Metro-Goldwyn-Mayer
    d. Warner Bros.

8. Itzhak (Jack) Warner was born in Poland, emigrated with his siblings to Canada, opened a movie theater in Pennsylvania in 1903, and eventually created what company?

    a. Fox Filmed Entertainment
    b. Sony Pictures
    c. Warner Bros.
    d. NBC Universal

9. Who is Allan Stewart Konigsberg?

a. Woody Allen
b. Larry David
c. Larry King
d. Allen Ginsberg

10. Who is Issur Danielovitch Demsky?

a. Sid Caesar
b. Mel Brooks
c. Kirk Douglas
d. Milton Berle

11. Betty Joan Perske, the cousin of Israeli prime minister and Nobel Prize winner Shimon Peres, is better know by what name?

a. Lauren Bacall
b. Shelley Winters
c. Gracie Fields
d. Fanny Brice

12. Where did comedian Jack Benny meet his wife, Sadye (Sadie) Marks?

a. Times Square
b. Hollywood
c. In synagogue with Groucho Marx
d. A Passover *Seder* with Zeppo Marx

13. Who said the following: "Before I speak, I have something important to say."

a. Groucho Marx
b. Jon Stewart
c. Susan Sontag
d. Irving Stone

14. Who was the host of NBC's *Texaco Star Theater*?

a. Walter Lippmann
b. George Jean Nathan
c. Abraham Cahan
d. Milton Berle

15. Which Jewish painter painted the ceiling for the Paris Opera in 1963?

a. Marc Chagall
b. Solomon Nunes Carvalho
c. Henry Mosler
d. Sir Jacob Epstein

16. Poet Emma Lazarus is best known for "The New Colossus," a sonnet inscribed on the pedestal of what American treasure?

a. The Liberty Bell
b. Grant's Tomb
c. The Pentagon
d. The Statue of Liberty

17. Which entertainer also wrote the book *Handcuff Secrets*?

a. Sarah Silverman
b. Charlie Chaplin
c. Harry Houdini
d. Al Franken

18. Who was one of the most famous names in American burlesque?

a. Estelle Getty
b. Florenz (Flo) Ziegfield
c. Elon Gold
d. Bette Midler

19. Comedian and actor Adam Sandler is famous for his song about what Jewish holiday?

a. *Hanukkah*
b. Passover
c. *Purim*
d. *Yom Kippur*

20. What instrument does Isaac Stern play?

a. Guitar
b. Violin
c. Drums
d. Saxophone

21. Which of the following Neil Simon plays was also a TV series?

a. *The Sunshine Boys*
b. *The Odd Couple*
c. *Brighton Beach Memoirs*
d. *Barefoot in the Park*

Steven Spielberg

In a career that spans decades, Steven Spielberg reigns supreme as one of Hollywood's greatest storytellers/directors. His films cover every genre—science fiction to action-adventure to comedy—and remain quintessentially Spielberg-ian at their core. As with any great artist, audiences recognize a Spielberg film from the first frame. Today, Spielberg is considered one of the most commercially successful filmmakers in Hollywood history. Not bad for a little Jewish boy from Ohio who used to charge 25 cents admission to his home movies.

Think you know everything there is to know about this Hollywood great? Try these on for size:

1. Which film featured Spielberg's wife-to-be, Kate Capshaw, as a main character?
2. Spielberg won his first Academy Award for Best Director for which film?
3. Who is Spielberg's famous god-daughter?
4. What is the name of the restaurant Spielberg owned? (Hint: It was located on Santa Monica Boulevard.)
5. What is the name of the kosher restaurant his mother owns in Los Angeles?
6. Which Michael Jackson video did Spielberg appear in?
7. What is the title of his first feature-length theater release?
8. How many Academy Awards was the *The Color Purple* nominated for?
9. What honor did Spielberg receive from France's President Nicolas Sarkozy in 2008?
10. What high school did Spielberg graduate from?

Answers

1. *Indiana Jones and the Temple of Doom*
2. *Schindler's List*
3. Drew Barrymore
4. Dive!
5. Milky Way
6. "Liberian Girl"
7. *The Sugarland Express* (1974)
8. Eleven
9. He was made an officer of the French Legion of Honor
10. California's Saratoga High School

22. In the Israeli version of *Sesame Street* (called *Rechov Sumsum*), who are Bert and Ernie?

a. Abraham and Akim
b. Balfour and Even
c. Bentz and Arik
d. Gal and Hadar

23. How many daughters does Tevye have in the play/film *Fiddler on the Roof*?

a. 5
b. 2
c. 3
d. 6

24. In the TV show *The Simpsons*, who was Krusty the Clown's father?

a. A vaudeville star
b. A rabbi
c. Woody Allen
d. Larry David

25. In an episode of the popular TV show *Seinfeld*, Jerry Seinfeld's parents are incredibly proud of their son, except for one occasion, for which they are appalled. What is this occasion?

a. When they find out Jerry pays his cleaning lady for more than just cleaning
b. When they find out Jerry has a rivalry with a man in a maroon VW Golf car
c. When they find out Jerry made out with his date during *Schindler's List*
d. When they find out Jerry cheats at the game Frogger

26. Who took over the hosting responsibilities of *The Daily Show* from Craig Kilborn in 1999?

a. Larry King
b. Stephen Colbert
c. Jon Stewart
d. Drew Birns

27. Which actor played the main character in Woody Allen's *Whatever Works*?

a. Zac Efron
b. Ben Stiller
c. Jerry Stiller
d. Larry David

28. What is the name of the production company started by Steven Spielberg, Jeffrey Katzenberg, and David Geffen?

a. Amblin
b. DreamWorks
c. Pixar
d. Miramax

29. Which famous director worked at the Howard Johnson's restaurant in New York's Times Square when he was 17 years old?

a. Mike Nichols
b. Larry David
c. Steven Spielberg
d. Carl Reiner

30. How many times has Bob Dylan performed in his hometown of Minneapolis since moving to New York in 1960?

a. 50

b. 10

c. 5

d. None

31. While serving in the U.S. Army, what department was Gene Wilder assigned to?

a. The Department of Psychiatry and Neurology

b. The Department of Science and Technology

c. The Department of Health

d. He was never in the U.S. Army

32. According to Hollywood folklore, what did the MGM commissary serve every day in honor of founder Louis B. Mayer's mother?

a. *Latkes*

b. *Borscht*

c. Chicken soup

d. Matzah ball soup

33. Director Otto Preminger's father was the first Jew to be appointed to what position?

a. Secretary of War of the Austrian Empire

b. U.S. Secretary of State

c. Chief prosecutor of the Austrian Empire

d. U.S. Chief of Staff

34. Christopher Plummer portrayed which American journalist in the 1999 film *The Insider*?

a. Henry Luce
b. Walter Cronkite
c. Mike Wallace
d. Bob Woodward

35. What year was Larry King inducted into the Radio Hall of Fame?

a. 2010
b. 1989
c. 1976
d. 2001

36. What was Barbra Streisand's character's profession in *The Mirror Has Two Faces*?

a. Teacher
b. Nurse
c. Professor
d. Housewife

37. Who used to babysit Billy Crystal when he was a child?

a. Barbra Streisand
b. Billie Holiday
c. Erica Jong
d. Bette Midler

38. Who was Carrie Fisher once engaged to?

a. Dan Aykroyd
b. Norman Mailer
c. E.L. Doctorow
d. Bill Murray

39. Who said the following: "Anybody can direct, but there are only eleven good writers."

a. Ben Stiller
b. Mel Brooks
c. Woody Allen
d. Natalie Portman

40. This actor's first uncredited role was in the film *Criss Cross* (1949). He played a rumba dancer. Who is he?

a. Lenny Bruce
b. Rodney Dangerfield
c. Tony Curtis
d. Don Rickles

41. Which performer said the following: "I have no religion. But culturally I can't escape it; I'm very Jewish."

a. Sarah Silverman
b. Lenny Bruce
c. Carl Reiner
d. Sacha Baron Cohen

42. Which of the following actors is known for playing Benjamin Braddock?

a. Liev Schreiber
b. Albert Brooks
c. Gene Wilder
d. Dustin Hoffman

43. What are the real names of The Marx Brothers—Groucho, Harpo, and Chico?

a. Max, Bernie, and Leonard
b. Julius, Arthur, and Leonard
c. Barry, Leonard, and Anthony
d. Isaac, Larry, and Ed

44. Which performer started his career in the Cleveland Playhouse and would later go on to originate the role of the Master of Ceremonies in the musical *Cabaret*?

a. Joel Grey
b. Walter Matthau
c. Tony Randall
d. Zero Mostel

45. What song did Sophie Tucker make famous?

a. "A Yiddishe Mamme"
b. "Sugar in My Bowl"
c. "I Love You, Porgy"
d. "My Baby Just Cares for Me"

46. What is the "Borscht Belt"?

a. Broadway in the 1920s
b. The Catskills
c. New York City's Bowery in the 1930s
d. A type of cocktail—vodka and cranberry—served at speakeasies in the 1950s

47. What Martin Scorsese film featured Jerry Lewis, Robert De Niro, and Sandra Bernhard?

    a. *The King of Comedy*
    b. *The Last Temptation of Christ*
    c. *After Hours*
    d. *New York Stories*

48. What year did Jack Benny die?

    a. 1980
    b. 1992
    c. 1963
    d. 1974

49. Where is Leonard Bernstein buried?

    a. Cypress Hills Cemetery in Brooklyn
    b. Green-Wood Cemetery in Brooklyn
    c. Mount Olivet Cemetery in Maspeth, Queens
    d. Woodlawn Cemetery in the Bronx

50. Which bandleader was known as "The King of Swing"?

    a. Louis Jordan
    b. Benny Goodman
    c. Stan Kenton
    d. Artie Shaw

51. What did Adolph Ochs publish, beginning in 1896?

    a. *The Wall Street Journal*
    b. *The New York Sun*
    c. *The New York Times*
    d. *The New York Post*

52. Who are the Pulitzer prizes named after?

a. Max Pulitzer
b. Larry Pulitzer
c. Joseph Pulitzer
d. Leonard Pulitzer

53. What did Mr. Pulitzer (of #52 above) found in 1903?

a. The Columbia School of Journalism
b. New York University
c. The New School for Social Research
d. The Art Students League of New York

54. What is *Heeb?*

a. A satirical album of comedy by Ben Stiller
b. A Jewish magazine aimed at young, hip adults
c. A book by Irving Stone
d. A compilation of essays by Bernard Malamud

55. What magazine did Isaac Bashevis Singer's writing first appear in?

a. *The New Yorker*
b. *Forward*
c. *The Nation*
d. *Playboy*

56. What is Shalom Rabinovich's pseudonym?

a. Leon Uris
b. Mark Helprin
c. Shalom Aleichem
d. Irwin Shaw

57. Rabinovich is most famous for writing what?

a. *War and Remembrance*
b. *West Side Story*
c. *The Producers*
d. *Tevye the Dairyman*

58. Who wrote *A Social and Religious History of the Jews*?

a. Salo W. Baron
b. Tillie Olsen
c. S. J. Perelman
d. Lionel Trilling

59. Which Philip Roth book won the National Book Award in 1959?

a. *Portnoy's Complaint*
b. *The Human Stain*
c. *Goodbye, Columbus*
d. *American Pastoral*

60. What did Saul Bellow win in 1976?

a. The Nobel Prize for Literature
b. The PEN Award
c. National Jewish Book Award
d. National Book Award

61. Erica Jong is perhaps best known for her first book, which is titled?

a. *How to Save Your Own Life*
b. *Inventing Memory*
c. *At the Edge of the Body*
d. *Fear of Flying*

62. Robert Altman credits which book as influencing his own comedy *M*A*S*H*?

a. *Catch-22* by Joseph Heller
b. *War and Remembrance* by Herman Wouk
c. *Exodus* by Leon Uris
d. *The Naked and the Dead* by Norman Mailer

63. Which of the following writers, a member of the Algonquin Round Table, was famous for her pithy remarks and for her book reviews in *The New Yorker* under the "Constant Reader" byline?

a. Susan Sontag
b. Diana Trilling
c. Dorothy Parker
d. Cynthia Ozick

64. What is the first line to Allen Ginsberg's iconic poem *Howl*?

a. "It was love at first sight…"
b. "Oh the sisters of mercy, they are not departed or gone…"
c. "I saw the best minds of my generation destroyed by madness, starving hysterical naked…"
d. "I got this graveyard woman, you know she keeps my kid…"

65. Which writer and artist illustrated Else Holmelund Minarik's *Little Bear* series of books?

a. Peter Max
b. Dorothy Parker
c. Esphyr Slobodkina
d. Maurice Sendak

66. Besides being a leader in the psychedelic movement in art and graphic design, which artist famously owns a collection of 36 Chevrolet Corvettes, dating from 1953 to 1988, one for each year?

a. Peter Max
b. Cindy Sherman
c. Sol LeWitt
d. Heinz Edelmann

67. Richard Avedon, the famous photographer, attended DeWitt Clinton High School in the Bronx, where he worked on the school paper with which of the following famous writers?

a. Ernest Hemingway
b. James Baldwin
c. John Steinbeck
d. Truman Capote

68. Irving Penn most famously took fashion photographs for which magazine?

a. *Vogue*
b. *Glamour*
c. *Women's Wear Daily*
d. *Harper's Bazaar*

69. What did philanthropist Benjamin Altman donate to the Metropolitan Museum in 1913?

a. A rare Egyptian scarab
b. The painting *Washington Crossing the Delaware*
c. His personal art collection
d. Hokusai's *The Great Wave off Kanagawa*

70. When Max Weber held a one-man exhibit of his work in 1911, it was considered to be too what?

a. Colorful
b. Realistic
c. Modern
d. Impressionistic

71. Who was married to Georgia O'Keefe?

a. Diego Rivera
b. Jackson Pollock
c. Philip Roth
d. Alfred Stieglitz

72. Who wrote *The Naked and the Dead* and *The Deer Park?*

a. Norman Mailer
b. Joseph Heller
c. Leon Uris
d. Bernard Malamud

73. Who did Herman Wouk dedicate his book *War and Remembrance* to, with these famous words: "He will destroy death forever."

a. His son
b. His wife
c. His mother
d. His father

74. Who is the main character in Chaim Potok's book *The Chosen*?

a. Philip Pirrip
b. Oskar Schell
c. Reuven Malter
d. Holden Caulfield

75. In the musical *Fiddler on the Roof,* what did Motel buy to make more money?

a. A sewing machine
b. An iron
c. A broom
d. A horse

CHAPTER FOUR

We Are the Champions: Sports

"To win. Nothing else matters, and nothing else will do."
—Sandy Koufax

A dmit it: You're surprised this chapter even exists, right? Ever since Los Angeles Dodger Sandy Koufax refused to pitch on *Yom Kippur* during the World Series and ignited Jewish pride the world over, few things upset Jewish sports fans than disbelief in our athletic abilities. To date, there are a number of Jewish Sports Halls of Fames in the United States, tons of websites and blogs dedicated to tracking our sporting prowess, and a newly issued set of Jewish Major Leaguers' baseball cards covering the years 1970 to 2003. This is big business.

We've included trivia on everything from chess and poker to boxing and swimming, even bullfighting. After all, any sport is meaningless without a little mental competition…and an angry bull or two.

1. **Who was the youngest former player to be inducted into the Baseball Hall of Fame?**

   a. Brad Ausmus
   b. Ryan Braun
   c. Sandy Koufax
   d. Matt Ford

2. **What did swimmer Mark Spitz do in 1972?**

   a. Won a gold medal at the Munich Olympics
   b. Won a silver medal at the Munich Olympics
   c. Won a bronze medal at the Munich Olympics
   d. Won seven gold medals at the Munich Olympics

3. **Which baseball catcher was the first catcher to stand up close to the batter at all times and throw from a crouching stance?**

   a. Johnny Bench
   b. Johnny Kling
   c. Lloyd Waner
   d. Chuck Klein

4. **Who was known as the first power forward of the NBA?**

   a. Troy Murphy
   b. Dolph Schayes
   c. Elvin Hayes
   d. Jerry Lucas

5. **Who was the first Jewish ballplayer to be elected to the Hall of Fame?**

   a. Joe Cronin
   b. Red Ruffing
   c. Hank Greenberg
   d. Hack Wilson

6. Which Yankee slugger was known as the "Kosher Bomber"?

    a. Ron Bloomberg
    b. Bernie Williams
    c. Graig Nettles
    d. Roger Maris

7. Which light-heavyweight champ boxer of the 1970s wore a Star of David on his trunks and called himself the "Jewish Bomber"?

    a. Scott Buck
    b. Zab Judah
    c. Moe Ginsberg
    d. Mike Rossman

8. Who is the only Jewish quarterback to lead his team to an NFL Championship?

    a. Jay Fiedler
    b. Sage Rosenfels
    c. Sid Luckman
    d. Hayden Epstein

9. How many Israeli athletes were massacred at the Munich Olympics in 1972?

    a. 11
    b. 2
    c. 5
    d. 15

10. Who said the following upon defeating the Moscow basketball team in 1977: "We are on the map and staying on the map in sports and all else"?

a. Red Auerbach
b. David Bluthenthal
c. Tal Brody
d. Tal Burstein

11. Which boxer was the lightweight boxing champion of the world who retained his crown for more than seven years before retiring?

a. Benny Leonard
b. George "Kid" Ashe
c. Ron "The Yid Kid" Aurit
d. Benny "Little Fish" Bass

12. Which Jewish wrestler won the World Championship Wrestling title from Hulk Hogan?

a. Max Bloom
b. Rob Feinstein
c. Bill Goldberg
d. Boris Malenko

13. What did Agnes Keleti accomplish in the 1940s and 1950s?

a. She won 10 medals in 3 Olympiads
b. She became the first woman to sail around the world 3 consecutive times
c. She won Wimbledon
d. She became the first woman to place in Olympiad archery

14. Which bullfighter was actually from Brooklyn and was praised by Ernest Hemingway for his skill and showmanship?

a. Manuel Granero
b. Francisco Rivera
c. Joe Escalante
d. Sidney Franklin

15. What was Football Hall-of-Famer Phil King's alma mater?

a. Harvard
b. Princeton
c. Yale
d. Columbia

16. What Jewish pitcher played in the Mexican Leagues under the name Pablo Garcia?

a. Adam Greenberg
b. Al Levine
c. Syd Cohen
d. Bob Melvin

17. What was pitcher Barney Pelty's nickname?

a. "The Yiddish Curver"
b. "The Flame Thrower"
c. "The Wily One"
d. "The Chosen"

18. What happened in the world of chess on March 10, 2005?

a. Garry Kimovich Kasparov became an International Grand Master
b. Garry Kimovich Kasparov won the World Championship
c. Garry Kimovich Kasparov beat Bobby Fischer
d. Garry Kimovich Kasparov retired

19. Who did Kasparov famously lose to in a 1997 match?

a. Viswanathan Anand
b. Deep Blue, a computer developed by IBM
c. Wilhelm Steinitz
d. Mikhail Botvinnik

20. David Barry and Hautzig Berg published a book titled *Opening Moves: The Making of a Young Chess Champion*. Who was the book written about?

a. Michael Thaler
b. Paul Morphy
c. Bobby Fischer
d. Rustam Kasimdzhanov

21. Why is Motti Kakkon, a soccer player, called "the vulture"?

a. He dips in and out of the field like a vulture
b. He has a fierce, predatory style in the box
c. He has an ear-piercing, celebratory screech
d. His hair is as black as a vulture

22. Who is Avi Nimni?

a. A world-famous swimmer
b. A two-time Olympian in track and field
c. Israel's most prominent basketball player
d. One of Maccabi Tel Aviv's greatest soccer players

23. What is Mathieu Schneider's claim to fame?

a. He is the all-time leading Jewish scorer in NHL history
b. He is the all-time leading Jewish scorer in NBA history
c. He is the all-time leading Jewish scorer in USTA history
d. He is the all-time leading Jewish scorer in NFL history

24. Generally considered one of the greatest coaches in the history of NBA, what did Red Auerbach do?

    a. Guided Detroit Pistons to victories in the 1989 and 1990 NBA finals

    b. Created the Boston Celtics dynasty that won nine NBA championships (eight of them consecutive) over ten years

    c. Served 18 seasons as head coach of the Knicks

    d. Led four L.A. Lakers teams to victory

25. Which junior middleweight wears a Star of David on his boxing trunks?

    a. Al "Bummy" Davis

    b. "Mad" Max Heyman

    c. Yuri Foreman

    d. Art Lasky

26. Who famously said, "Just win, baby"?

    a. Bruce Pearl

    b. Red Auerbach

    c. Seth Greenberg

    d. Allen Davis

27. Besides being considered one of Israel's top female tennis players, Anna Smashnova (now Anna Pistolesi) speaks which three languages?

    a. French, Russian, and Hebrew

    b. Russian, English, and Hebrew

    c. French, Russian, and English

    d. French, Russian, and Hebrew

Brooklyn Bullfighter

✡

Have you heard the one about the Jewish matador from Brooklyn? From the 1920s through the 1950s, Sidney Franklin of Park Slope gained international fame as the Bullfighter from Brooklyn. Though he never fought a bull in Brooklyn, he did conquer a slice of Spain in 1929, after making a spectacular debut in Seville that year. His courage was immortalized by Ernest Hemingway's *Death in the Afternoon*. Hemmingway wrote, "Sidney Franklin is brave, with a cold, serene, and intelligent valor. No history of bullfighting that is ever written can be complete unless it gives him the space he is entitled to."

Eager to show off his skill in the United States, Franklin staged a series of A.S.P.C.A.-approved bull-dodging exhibitions at the 1939 World's Fair in Flushing Meadows, New York, where he fared much better than his far more violent Spanish headliner shows. During the course of his career, he was gored seriously four times and had several surgeries. He died at the age of 72 in a Greenwich Village nursing home.

28. **What record does Bob Dover hold?**

   a. He competed in six consecutive Olympiads for the U.S. equestrian team

   b. He holds the record for the longest windsurfing journey (5,045 miles)

   c. He holds the record for the longest distance rowed in 24 hours (163.42 miles)

   d. He holds the record for the most concrete blocks broken in one minute (888 blocks)

29. Which of the following is considered one of the world's best sabre fencers?

a. Sergei Charikov
b. Elaine Cheris
c. Daniel Bukantz
d. Shlomo Eyal

30. What were Joe Jacobi and his partner, Scott Strausbaugh, the first Americans to accomplish?

a. They were the first American team in Olympic history to capture a gold medal in rowing
b. They were the first American team in Olympic history to capture a gold medal in whitewater slalom
c. They were the first American team in Olympic history to capture a gold medal in the luge
d. They were the first American team in Olympic history to capture a gold medal in curling

31. Guy Starek is considered one of Israel's top athletes in what sport?

a. Shooting
b. Archery
c. Swimming
d. Soccer

32. Who was the Women's International Grand Master in chess in 1985?

a. Elena Ahmilovskaya
b. Agneshka Brustman
c. Eva Aronson
d. Lucille Kellner

33. Where was Scott Feldman, a right-handed pitcher for the Texas Rangers, born?

    a. Denver, Colo.
    b. Chicago, Ill.
    c. Kailua, Hawaii
    d. Anchorage, Alaska

34. What did Max Heyman accomplish at age eight, making him the youngest person in the U.S. to do so?

    a. He circumnavigated the world
    b. He threw the opening pitch at Yankee Stadium
    c. He got his black belt at the Japan Karate Association
    d. He set the record for the most vaults in an hour

35. Who is Josh Miller?

    a. A left-footed punter for the Tennessee Titans
    b. A shortstop for the New York Yankees
    c. A world-famous poker champion
    d. The youngest chess champion to win a match against Bobby Fischer

36. What did Lee Korsitz win in 2003?

    a. The World Championship title for Texas Hold 'Em
    b. The World Figure Skating Championship title
    c. The Formula One World Championship title
    d. The World Women's Mistral Championship title

37. A three-time world champion, Karen Leibovitch is considered the greatest Israeli Paralympic athlete of all time. How did she injure her legs?

a. In a car accident
b. During her service in the Israel Defense Forces, while training to be an officer
c. She didn't injure them; she was born paralyzed
d. In a skydiving accident

38. Who was the first Israeli to be drafted by an NHL team (the New Jersey Devils)?

a. Jeff Halpern
b. Mathieu Schneider
c. Max Birbraer
d. Steve Dubinksy

39. Why is former soccer player Alon Mizrahi called "the airplane"?

a. His arm span is incredibly long, like that of an airplane's wingspan
b. His father was an airplane pilot
c. He swoops in to make goals
d. When he made a goal, he celebrated his victory by mimicking an airplane

40. Which Israeli soccer player is known for his outspoken political opinions?

a. Eli Ohana
b. Yossi Abuksis
c. Pini Balili
d. Tal Banin

41. What magazine cover in 1999 featured soccer player Sara Whalen hugging Brandi Chastain?

a. *Shape*
b. *O*
c. *Time*
d. *Glamour*

42. Who is Andy Ram's doubles partner?

a. Gaston Etlis
b. Jonathan Erlich
c. Paul Goldstein
d. Harel Levy

43. Born to Holocaust survivors, Ernest Grunfeld is the general manager for what basketball team

a. The New York Knicks
b. The Chicago Bulls
c. The Washington Wizards
d. The Orlando Magic

44. Who is the Israeli "Ice Man"?

a. Andy Cohen
b. Scott Feldman
c. Hank Greenberg
d. Doron Sheffer

45. After knocking out British champ Isaac Sebasduka in 37 seconds of the first round, what did Nicolai Melandovich do?

a. He never fought professionally again
b. He observed *Shabbat*
c. He retired and became a stockbroker
d. He famously exclaimed, "This is my house!"

46. What does boxer Dmitriy Salita do on Shabbat?

a. Attends synagogue services
b. Recites *Kiddush* over a cup of wine
c. Refuses to fight
d. All of the above

47. Who is popularly considered to be the greatest Jewish tennis player in history?

a. Dick Savitt
b. Jess Salzenstein
c. Jay Berger
d. Jesse Levine

48. Alla Shulimovna Kushnir was the 1970 USSR champion in what sport?

a. Archery
b. Chess
c. Figure Skating
d. Gymnastics

49. Which Olympic wrestler competed for a dozen years without ever losing a match?

a. Abe Ford
b. Bennie "Crusher" Feldman
c. Henry Wittenberg
d. Mighty Atlas

50. Which Jewish pitcher played for the Chicago Cubs, 1965–71?

a. Ken Holtzman
b. Phil Cooney
c. Ross Baumgarten
d. Ron Blomberg

CHAPTER FIVE

But Is It Kosher?: Food

"The remarkable thing about my mother is that for thirty years she served us nothing but leftovers. The original meal has never been found." —Calvin Trillin

First, let's be clear on one thing: Delicious Jewish food is not an oxymoron. And, yes, all Jewish mothers include a generous side dish of old-fashioned guilt with every meal served. This is just a fact of nature. The staples of American Jewish food are some of the best stuff there is—chicken noodle soup, *latkes*, bialys, and bagels—never mind the liver and fried onion, gefilte fish, and creamed herring. These kosher noshes conjure childhood memories, evenings spent with family and friends, the low flicker of *Seder* candlelight. And nothing's better than that.

1. **What type of food is typically served on *Lag B'Omer*?**

   a. Grilled food
   b. Oily food
   c. Sweet food
   d. Salty food

2. **Where did *Sabich*—a popular Israeli food made with eggplant, egg, and hummus—originate?**

   a. Iran
   b. Greece
   c. Ukraine
   d. Iraq

3. **What is *kashrut*?**

   a. The law of keeping food kosher
   b. A prayer said before Passover *Seder*
   c. A type of dessert
   d. A type of appetizer

4. **The kitchens of observant Orthodox Jews are divided to keep what types of food separate from one another?**

   a. Fish and dairy
   b. Meat and grain
   c. Meat and dairy
   d. Grain and dairy

5. **In accordance with Jewish law, meat must be completely drained of what before it is eaten?**

   a. Fat
   b. Blood
   c. Water
   d. Toxins

6. Founded in 1888, which company is the world's largest kosher brand and manufacturer of *matzah*?

    a. Go 4 Kosher

    b. Manischewitz

    c. Sinai Kosher

    d. Aron Streit, Inc.

7. What type of grape is used to make Manischewitz wine?

    a. Labrusca grapes

    b. Greco Nero grapes

    c. Rabosco grapes

    d. Limnio grapes

8. What is the significance of serving pomegranates during *Rosh Hashana*?

    a. The number of seeds in the fruit—613—corresponds to the number of *mitzvot* (rules) in the Torah

    b. Pomegranates signal good luck

    c. There is no significance

    d. The color red is considered holy

9. Before the fast of *Tisha B'av*, observant Ashkenazi Jews sometimes eat hard-boiled eggs sprinkled with what?

    a. Salt

    b. Parsley

    c. Thyme

    d. Ashes

10. What is *smetana*?

    a. Jam

    b. Butter

    c. Cream cheese

    d. Heavy sour cream

11. When a food is considered *pareve*, what is it?

    a. It contains neither dairy nor meat products

    b. It contains neither dairy nor grain products

    c. It contains no dairy product

    d. It has been blessed by a rabbi

12. What is the only bread product to be boiled before it is baked?

    a. Bagel

    b. *Knish*

    c. Pretzel

    d. Donut

13. What does the word *challah* refer to in the Bible?

    a. God

    b. The hole in a bagel

    c. The portion of dough set aside for the *kohen*

    d. A type of *matzah*

14. What dish is commonly referred to as Jewish penicillin?

    a. Chicken soup

    b. Borscht

    c. Minestrone soup

    d. Split pea soup

An Ode to the Bagel

✡

P aris has its baguettes and Dublin its soda bread. San Francisco has perfected the sourdough and Chicago the deep dish. But no city and no culture so closely identifies with the bagel than New York and Jews. While the derivation of the word "bagel" is unclear, its tastiness is undisputed. Joan Nathan, author of *Jewish Cooking in America* says the word come from the German verb *biegen*, "to bend." Other possibilities include the Yiddish *beygel*, taken from the German *beugel*, meaning "ring" or "bracelet." If the etymology of the word weren't unclear enough, there is still the issue of origin—some lore suggests the bagel was invented in 1683 by a Jewish baker in Vienna. If you listen to my *bubbe*, she'll tell you my family invented the bagel while running from the Turks in Russia. No matter. There is one indisputable fact that makes all else obsolete: Eastern European immigrants arriving on the streets of New York's Lower East Side at the turn of the twentieth century brought the bagel with them. There, they were baked and sold on the streets on sticks. The rest, as they say, is history.

15. Which of the following is a Ukranian word for "dumpling"?

a. *Kugel*
b. *Hamantaschen*
c. *Kreplach*
d. *Knish*

16. Which dish is a common stew eaten during *Shabbat*?

a. *Bigos*
b. *Baeckeoffe*
c. *Cholent*
d. *Kasha Varnishkas*

17. Traditionally, what color is *tzimmes*?

a. Orange
b. Purple
c. Yellow
d. Green

18. In Yiddish, what does *tzimmes* mean?

a. A big fuss
b. Awful food
c. Junk food
d. To simmer

19. In 1907, Joel Russ began selling mushrooms on strings in New York City's Lower East Side. He eventually saved up enough money to operate a pushcart and then a horse and wagon. In 1914, he opened what legendary New York epicurean institution?

a. H&H Bagels
b. Russ & Daughters
c. Gus's Pickles
d. 2nd Avenue Deli

20. In 2002, former *New York Times* food writer Mimi Sheraton wrote a book that detailed the history of what famous Jewish staple?

a. Bialys
b. Seltzer
c. Decaf coffee
d. Bagels

21. Complete this famous Psalm: "My cup..."

a. ...is half empty."
b. ...my cup. My Kingdom for a cup."
c. ...is half full."
d. ...runneth over."

22. What are Kasha Varnishkes?

a. Grits and spaghetti
b. Franks and beans
c. Oatmeal and orzo
d. Buckwheat and bowtie pasta

23. During *Hanukkah*, it is common to serve the Sephardic treat of big, puffy jelly doughnuts. What is this dessert called?

a. *Sufganiyot*
b. *Katchka*
c. *Kugel*
d. *Hamentaschen*

24. Complete this sentence: Observant Jews may eat only meat of animals that chew their cud and have cloven hooves, which eliminates pigs, horses, and rabbits, whose meat is considered...

a. Too fatty
b. Unsavory
c. Too gamey
d. Forbidden

25. What is the *shochet*'s principle job?

a. To slaughter all meat and poultry for kosher consumption
b. To distribute candy to children
c. To bless meat for consumption
d. To pickle vegetables

26. The term *glatt kosher* is broadly applied to mean the strictest observance of food. If a food is deemed to be *glatt kosher*, which part of the animal has been inspected after slaughter?

a. The brain
b. The blood
c. The fur
d. The lungs

27. Fresh and saltwater fish are considered *pareve*, but to be kosher, what must they have?

a. Silver-colored scales
b. A minimum length of six inches
c. Fins and overlapping scales that can be removed while leaving the skin intact
d. Whiskers

28. The original ingredients used by cooks in the land of Israel include the seven biblical foods mentioned in Deuteronomy. What are these seven foods?

a. Barley, apples, figs, dates, pomegranates, olives, and oranges
b. Barley, apples, figs, dates, pomegranates, olives, and almonds
c. Barley, almonds, figs, dates, pomegranates, olives, and persimmons
d. Barley, wheat, figs, dates, pomegranates, olives, and grapes

29. What does the Yiddish word *forshpeis* mean?

a. After food
b. Dessert
c. Before food
d. The main course

30. What did Max Asnas do in 1937?

a. He operated New York's first licensed pretzel cart
b. He made the world's tallest pastrami sandwich
c. He opened New York City's Stage Deli
d. His restaurant catered for a group of dignitaries watching a boxing match in Madison Square Garden

31. What famous New York City restaurant and deli is commonly referred to as "The Sturgeon King"?

a. Katz's Deli
b. Russ & Daughters
c. 2nd Avenue Deli
d. Barney Greengrass

32. What is *matzah brie*, a Passover treat, commonly called?

    a. Passover muffin
    b. Passover pancakes
    c. Passover oatmeal
    d. Passover scrambled eggs

33. What classic New York City restaurant was the site of Meg Ryan and Billy Crystal's famous "I'll have what she's having" scene in the 1989 film *When Harry Met Sally*?

    a. Carnegie Deli
    b. Ben's Kosher Deli
    c. Kosher Deluxe
    d. Katz's Deli

34. In 2002, Guss Pickles—the famous New York City sidewalk stand started by Izzy Guss in early 1910—moved from which street to which street?

    a. The Bowery to Canal Street
    b. Essex Street to Orchard Street
    c. Essex Street to Canal Street
    d. The Bowery to Orchard Street

35. What did Helmer Toro found in 1972?

    a. H&H Bagels
    b. Stage Deli
    c. Artie's Deli
    d. Junior's

36. **Max Asnas, the original owner of New York City's Stage Deli, was the first restaurateur to do what?**

   a. To put a celebrity sandwich on the menu
   b. To serve Passover *Seder*
   c. To put an egg cream on the menu
   d. To serve pickles and coleslaw gratis on the table

37. **Attman's Delicatessen is located in an area of East Baltimore affectionately known as what?**

   a. Pastrami Pastures
   b. The Bialy Belt
   c. Baltimore's Bagel Belt (BBB)
   d. Corned Beef Row

38. **In Los Angeles, regulars like Neil Diamond and Larry King frequent this stand-by. What is the name of this restaurant?**

   a. Canter's Deli
   b. Nate 'n Al Delicatessen
   c. Langer's Deli
   d. Pico Kosher Deli

39. **What made Ben Canter and his two brothers move to Los Angeles from New Jersey to open Canter's Deli, one of California's oldest delis?**

   a. The both married California girls
   b. The wanted to cater to the Hollywood crowd
   c. They lost their original Jersey deli in the 1929 stock market crash and looked to California for better fortunes
   d. They detested New York summers

40. Who said this humorous line: "Anytime a person goes into a delicatessen an orders a pastrami on white bread, somewhere a Jew dies."

a. Milton Berle
b. Mel Brooks
c. Lenny Bruce
d. John Stewart

41. What is Jewish speck?

a. A salt-dusted hard-boiled egg
b. Cow's tongue
c. Chicken feet
d. Paprika-dusted, twice-smoked slices of pickled fat from a brisket

42. What kind of sauce is Tongue Polonaise served in?

a. Garlic sauce
b. Tomato sauce
c. Sweet raisin sauce
d. Horseradish sauce

43. What beverage was originally billed as "2 Cents Plain"?

a. Seltzer
b. Club soda
c. Egg cream
d. Red wine

44. Complete the sentence. A nibbler is a...

a. Type of appetizer
b. Nosher
c. Person who eats with great gusto
d. Aperitif

45. This "Jewish Champagne" was first produced in 1868 in Brooklyn. The Food and Drug Administration objected to the beverage being called a tonic and, so, in the 1900s, the name was changed to which of the following?

a. Dr. Brown's Cel-Ray Soda
b. Dr. Brown's Cream Soda
c. Dr. Brown's Black Cherry Soda
d. Dr. Brown's Root Beer Soda

46. While it contains no eggs or cream, this "poor man's ice cream soda" originated in New York. What is it?

a. Milkshake
b. Egg Cream
c. Lime Rickey
d. Shirley Temple

47. Complete the traditional way to order a bagel: "I would like a bagel, please, with a _____ of cream cheese."

a. Ton
b. A lot
c. Schmear
d. Dab

48. In 1976, Abe Lebewohl, owner of New York City's 2nd Avenue Deli, donated 350 pounds of chopped liver to *New York* magazine designer Milton Glaser. What did Glaser do with the liver?

a. He hosted an art show called "Man and Liver" for which various artists created sculptures out of the food
b. He won the Guinness Book of World Records for the most liver sandwiches created in a day (888)
c. He donated it to a local homeless shelter
d. He built a scaled-down replica of the Statue of Liberty

49. What is lox?

a. Smoked salmon
b. Fried sturgeon
c. White fish
d. Tuna

50. What tragic accident occurred at New York City's 2nd Avenue Deli?

a. An employee was locked inside for over 48 hours
b. The founder, Abe Lebewohl, was killed during a robbery
c. A customer sued for a slip-and-fall accident and nearly made the restaurant go bankrupt
d. An employee suffered a heart attack while serving a table of customers

CHAPTER SIX

It's All Relative: Science and Medicine

"Dreams are often most profound when they seem the most crazy."
—Sigmund Freud

The comedian and actor Robin Williams once said, "Freud: If it's not one thing, it's your mother." Sigmund Freud, of course, paved the way for the future of psychoanalysis—and guilt complexes for every Jewish child. Beside Freud, there are lots of other heavy hitters in the field of science and medicine, like Jonas Salk, Albert Einstein, and J. Robert Oppenheimer. Some say science and medicine are relative fields—an especially apt statement when so much of it is dominated by a single culture.

1. **What did scientist Alfred Einhorn create?**

    a. Novocain
    b. Aspirin
    c. Melatonin
    d. Morphine

2. **Which scientist was awarded the Nobel Prize in Physics for discovering the exclusion principle?**

    a. Emile Berliner
    b. Donald A. Glaser
    c. Wolfgang Pauli
    d. Irving Janis

3. **Who is credited for being the first to use cocaine as a local anesthetic for surgery?**

    a. Ruben Katz
    b. Karl Koller
    c. Paul Rubenstein
    d. Joshua Lederberg

4. **Eric Kandel, the Austrian-born American neuroscientist, was awarded the Nobel Prize for his work on the physiological basis of memory storage in what?**

    a. Neurons
    b. Protons
    c. Neutrons
    d. Axons

5. Who is widely known for his general theory of relativity?

    a. Albert Einstein
    b. Phoebus Levene
    c. Eugene Wigner
    d. Franz Boas

6. When did Dan Shechtman discover the icosahedral phase?

    a. 1962
    b. 1972
    c. 1982
    d. 1992

7. What did William Herschel discover, besides infrared radiation?

    a. The Milky Way
    b. Uranus
    c. Laser-guided technology
    d. Greenhouse gases

8. Sheldon Lee Glashow is a notorious skeptic of what scientific theory?

    a. Big bang theory
    b. Atomic theory
    c. Antenna theory
    d. Superstring theory

9. Who invented the stencil duplicator (mimeograph)?

    a. David Gestetner
    b. Konrad Bloch
    c. Otto Warburg
    d. Emile Berliner

Albert Einstein

✡

Parents take note: Einstein was no Einstein when he was a kid. In fact, he was so slow in learning that his parents consulted a doctor, who promptly dubbed him, "the dopey one." Funny, but I don't see that doctor's name in any of the history books. Einstein's slow verbal development led to a lifelong habit of thinking in pictures rather than words. While many people might call such a habit "daydreaming," theoretical physicists have another name for it: "scientific experimentation." Much of Einstein's early scientific breakthroughs sprang from the imaginary experiments of his youth. Throughout his life, Einstein retained his childlike curiosity in the face of life's biggest mysteries. He often said that this quality helped him be a better scientist—a reminder that true genius is not just a function of intelligence but also of creativity and imagination.

10. **When was Einstein's general theory of relativity published?**

    a. 1936
    b. 1908
    c. 1915
    d. 1912

11. Who was the scientific director of the Manhattan Project?

a. Otto Stern
b. J. Robert Oppenheimer
c. Leopold Mannes
d. Fritz Perls

12. Who developed the first polio vaccine?

a. Jonas Salk
b. Norman Rubens
c. Edward Feigenbaum
d. Adam Cohen

13. When was Ervin Bauer's book *Theoretical Biology* published?

a. 1800
b. 1892
c. 1925
d. 1935

14. Which scientist became world famous for his popular science books and for the award-winning TV show *Cosmos: A Personal Voyage?*

a. Carl Sagan
b. Niels Bohr
c. Karl Koller
d. Edward Teller

15. Which Nobel Prize-winning chemist survived the Holocaust with help from his Ukrainian neighbors?

a. Paul Rubenstein
b. Roald Hoffman
c. Daniel Mandl
d. Kenneth Arrow

16. Which Hungarian physician and dermatologist was born to a Jewish family but converted to Catholicism?

a. Wolfgang Pauli
b. Dan Shechtman
c. Lise Meitner
d. Moritz Kaposi

17. Who is best known for his work *Stalking the Wild Pendulum: On the Mechanics of Consciousness*?

a. Jonathan Goldsmith
b. Itzhak Bentov
c. Juri Lotman
d. Peter Carl Goldmark

18. What did scientist George de Hevesy dissolve, when his home in Denmark was invaded by the Nazis, as a means of preventing the Nazis from stealing this prized possession?

a. His wedding ring
b. His father's gold Star of David
c. A golden cup
d. The Nobel Prizes won by Max von Laue and James Franck

19. Which doctor was, as a child, sent to Britain during World War II as the first of the Kindertransports to escape German anti-Semitism?

a. Leslie Brent
b. Zora Arkus-Duntov
c. Hollis Heartesty
d. Herbert Spencer Gasser

20. Who wrote and presented the BBC documentary series, *The Ascent of Man?*

a. Daniel Finkle
b. Donald A. Glaser
c. Jacob Bronowski
d. Ishmael Albertson

21. Before becoming an engineer and inventing the traveling-wave tube (TWT), Rudolf Kompfner trained in the study of what?

a. Architecture
b. Pediatrics
c. Physics
d. Astrology

22. Who developed the first *oral* polio vaccine?

a. Leopold Mannes
b. Carl Djerassi
c. Adam Cohen
d. Albert Sabin

23. Who was the first American to receive the Nobel Prize in the sciences?

a. Norman Rubens
b. Albert Abraham Michelson
c. Franz Boas
d. Douglas Osheroff

24. How old was Murray Gell-Mann when he entered Yale University?

a. 15
b. 18
c. 30
d. 62

25. What did J. Robert Oppenheimer—the father of the atomic bomb—call "Trinity"?

a. The first nuclear explosion at Alamagordo on July 16, 1945
b. His three children
c. Katherine Puening Harrison, his wife
d. The Lawrence Radiation Laboratory

26. What happened to Edward Teller—the father of the hydrogen bomb—that gave him a permanent limp?

a. Nothing; he didn't have a limp
b. He was born with a club foot
c. He was involved in a streetcar accident as a child and was forced to wear a prosthetic foot, which gave him a limp
d. He fell from a horse while riding to keep up with Hans Bethe

27. Who was considered a pioneer in the field of artificial intelligence?

a. Juri Lotman
b. Saul Amarel
c. Jared Diamond
d. Phoebus Levene

28. What group of animals did Dr. Oscar Auerbach train to smoke cigarettes as part of a study that proved the link between cigarette smoking and cancer?

a. Dogs
b. Monkeys
c. Mice
d. Ferrets

29. Who was awarded the Nobel Prize in physics for his services to theoretical physics and his discovery of the law of the photoelectric effect?

a. Robert Hofstadter
b. Gabriel Lippmann
c. Felix Bloch
d. Albert Einstein

30. Who is regarded as the father of cognitive therapy?

a. Franz Boas
b. Aaron Temkin Beck
c. Norman Rubens
d. Daniel Dalhoff

31. What hormone did Dr. Jeffrey M. Friedman discover that has been proven to have a role in regulating body weight?

a. Leptin
b. Carcitonin
c. Glucagon
d. Estrogen

32. What was the Seawolf, created by Henry Hurwitz Jr.?

a. The H-bomb
b. A nuclear submarine
c. A computer program and precursor to the Internet
d. A nuclear lab based at NORAD

33. What code did Marshall Warren Nirenberg, Har Gobind Khorana, and Robert W. Holley break?

a. The genetic code
b. The nomenclature code
c. The Morse code
d. The single-core code

34. Robert K. Merton was considered one of America's most influential social scientists. What was his birth name?

a. Meyer R. Schkolnick
b. Daniel Ellsberg
c. Herbert Simon
d. Dan Shechtman

35. Who did Einstein affectionately call "our Marie Curie" for her work on radioactivity and nuclear physics?

a. Rosalind Franklin
b. Sophie Germain
c. Lise Meitner
d. Rachel Carlson

36. Who, along with Stephen J. Gould, introduced the term "spandrel" into evolutionary theory?

a. David Lee
b. Richard Lewontin
c. Jonathan Goldsmith
d. Irving Janis

37. Who invented the Polaroid instant camera?

a. Claude Levi-Strauss
b. Ken Goldberg
c. Edwin H. Land
d. Emile Berliner

38. Saul Krugman discovered a vaccine for what?

a. Hepatitis B
b. Swine flu
c. Smallpox
d. Cholera

39. Who is known as the father of modern anthropology?

a. Robert Shechtman
b. Daniel Mandl
c. Dan Shechtman
d. Claude Levi-Strauss

40. Which microbiologist and immunologist made an important discovery regarding bacterial fertility factor F?

a. Melissa Franklin
b. Max Levchin
c. Esther Lederberg
d. Gregory Pincus

41. Who wrote the case history "Analysis of Phobia in a Five-Year-Old Boy"?

a. Abraham Maslow
b. Stanley Milgram
c. Sigmund Freud
d. Donald Ivey

42. Who is considered a top authority on scientific hydrotherapy?

a. Simon Baruch
b. Karl Koller
c. Joseph Erlanger
d. Edward Feigenbaum

43. Abraham Jacobi—the father of pediatrics—completed his autobiography in 1918, only to have what happen?

a. He died
b. His wife threw it—along with most of his personal possessions— out the window, and they scattered along New York City's Fifth Avenue
c. He lost it
d. A fire destroyed it, along with all of his personal notes and letters

44. Who is best known for his contributions to Einstein's theory of general relativity and developing the steady-state theory as an alternative to the big bang theory?

a. Hermann Bondi
b. Isidor Isaac Rabi
c. Emilio Segré
d. Hans Bethe

45. Which physicist is rumored to be the father of world chess champ Bobby Fischer?

a. Edward Feigenbaum
b. Ishmael Albertson
c. Karl Koller
d. Paul Nemenyi

46. In the wake of the Holocaust, what did Stanley Milgram test to great controversy?

a. Separation anxiety
b. Morals
c. Obedience
d. Deviance

47. Dr. Lynn Margulis' work on endosymbiotic theory formulation was the first to rely on what?

a. Direct paleontological observations
b. Direct microbiological observations
c. Direct zoological observations
d. Eukaryotic cells

48. Who characterized the different forms of nucleic acid, DNA from RNA, and found that DNA contained adenine, guanine, thymine, cytosine, deoxyribose, and a phosphate group?

a. Ferdinand Cohn
b. Phoebus Levene
c. Leopold Mannes
d. Norman Rubens

49. Along with Erwin Popper, who first isolated the polio virus?

    a. Daniel Mandl

    b. Tadeus Reichstein

    c. Harry Markowitz

    d. Karl Landsteiner

50. Who published *Atomic Energy Waste* in 1961?

    a. Charles Ivey

    b. Adam Cohen

    c. Eugen Glueckauf

    d. Jerome Friedman

CHAPTER SEVEN

If I Were a Rich Man: Business

> Perchik: Money is the world's curse.
> Teyve: May the Lord smite me with it.
> And may I never recover.
> —*Fiddler on the Roof*

Behind every prize-winning economist, there is usually a Jewish mother. More often than not, you can tell about the inner workings of a culture by the way its members handle their money. In the Jewish culture, money is the lifeblood; its what pays for that fancy Ivy League education, and, conversely, it is the root of all evil and Ponzi schemes. For a culture so fascinated by nickels and dimes, we are fortunate to have so many leaders who know how to manage it. Then you have my family: for me, money was never meant to be saved. It came beautifully wrapped in golden-colored foil every Passover and *Hanukkah*. Gelt was something you squandered and ate as soon as you got your hands on it. Maybe that's why I have to eat chocolate whenever I do my yearly taxes.

1. Who pioneered the modern portfolio theory?

    a. Milton Friedman

    b. Jacob Marschak

    c. Harry Markowitz

    d. Leonard Savage

2. Along with Peter Thiel, who is the co-founder of PayPal?

    a. Richard Lerner

    b. Max Levchin

    c. Luke Nosek

    d. Ken Howery

3. Who is the youngest person ever to win the Nobel Memorial Prize in Economics?

    a. Ben Bernanke

    b. Daniel Kahneman

    c. Matthew Rabin

    d. Kenneth Arrow

4. Who was the eighth richest person in the United States in 2008 and 2009?

    a. Michael Bloomberg

    b. Steve Ballmer

    c. Michael Dell

    d. David Geffen

5. What concept did Milton Friedman—the Nobel Prize-winning economist—advocate?

    a. The Keynesian theory

    b. The free market economy

    c. Microeconomics

    d. Game theory

6. What book did Benjamin Graham write with David Dodd?

    a. *International Economics: Theory and Policy*

    b. *Capitalism: A Treatise*

    c. *Security Analysis*

    d. *Game Change*

7. When did Alan Greenspan serve as Chairman of the Federal Reserve?

    a. 1976–1987

    b. 1987–1992

    c. 1992–2009

    d. 1987–2006

8. What did Steve Ballmer, CEO of Microsoft, do for the first time in 2009?

    a. He gave the keynote address at the Consumer Electronics Show

    b. He crossed the billion-dollar mark in net worth

    c. He sailed around the world

    d. He got married

9. Along with Larry Page, what did Sergey Brin, co-found?

    a. Facebook

    b. YouTube

    c. Google

    d. eBay

10. As a prominent music industry executive, who was instrumental in the careers of such artists as Alicia Keys, Whitney Houston, and Jennifer Hudson?

    a. Edgar Bronfman
    b. Clive Davis
    c. Jann Wenner
    d. Sacha Baron Cohen

11. Larry Ellison was co-founder of Oracle. What is Oracle?

    a. A major enterprise software company
    b. A book publishing company
    c. An independent movie production company
    d. A chain of department stores

12. Who is Stephen Alan Weinberg?

    a. A media mogul
    b. An American casino resort/real estate developer
    c. A New York City-based publisher
    d. A Wall Street hedge fund manager

13. What company did Sam Zell help found?

    a. Citigroup
    b. Bank of America
    c. Wells Fargo
    d. Equity Group Investments

14. Besides being co-founder of global advertising agency Saatchi & Saatchi, what else is Charles Saatchi known for?

   a. Owning the Saatchi Gallery
   b. Sponsoring NASCAR
   c. Owning a quarter stake in Churchill Downs
   d. Founding JetBlue Airways

15. Jeffrey Skoll was the first president of which company?

   a. Microsoft
   b. eBay
   c. Random House
   d. Etsy

16. Besides being the former CEO of SunAmerica, Eli Broad also is well-known for what?

   a. His philanthropic efforts
   b. A Wall Street insider trading scandal
   c. His prize-winning poker playing
   d. Being married to Elle MacPherson

17. How old was Michael Dell when his company ranked in *Fortune*'s list of the top 500 U.S. corporations?

   a. 21
   b. 27
   c. 30
   d. 35

18. Who is the operator of the largest Ponzi scheme in history?

   a. Jon Weldon James
   b. Scott Rothstein
   c. Bernard Madoff
   d. Kenneth Starr

19. Who was nicknamed the "Junk Bond King" by his critics?

a. Lloyd Blankfein
b. Michael Milken
c. Asher Edelman
d. Marcus Goldman

20. Which financial advisor has written seven *New York Times* bestsellers?

a. George Soros
b. Bruce Wasserstein
c. Samuel Sachs
d. Suze Orman

21. Who was charged with cheating customers and companies out of AUD $700 million in Australia's biggest ever cartel case?

a. Richard Pratt
b. Ronald Perelman
c. Marc Rich
d. Sheldon Adelson

22. What was George Soros' nickname after he made a reported $1 billion during Britain's 1992 Black Wednesday currency crisis?

a. "Lucky"
b. The "Man Who Broke the Bank of England"
c. The "Pretty Penny"
d. The "Man Who Got Away with It All"

23. Who wrote *A Passion to Win*?

a. Calvin Klein
b. Sumner Redstone
c. Howard Schultz
d. Sol Price

24. Julius Rosenwald was part-owner of which company?

a. Neiman-Marcus
b. J.C. Penny
c. Sears, Roebuck and Company
d. Kmart

25. Who is co-founder of Home Depot?

a. Steven Hirsch
b. Reuben Sturman
c. Sol Price
d. Bernie Marcus

26. What painting did Les Wexner, chairman and CEO of Limited Brands, donate to the Wexner Center for the Arts?

a. Picasso's *Nude on a Black Armchair*
b. Chagall's *The Fiddler*
c. Duchamp's *Nude Descending a Staircase*
d. Pollock's *No. 5, 1948*

27. What was Circuit City originally called?

a. Wards
b. Hardware City
c. Klein & Sons
d. P.C. Richard

Alan Greenspan

✡

As chairman of the Federal Reserve from 1987 to 2006, Alan Greenspan dominated the American economy and used strategic monetary policy to steer the economy through countless calamities: the Black Monday stock crash of 1987; the first Gulf War and its accompanying recession; the housing and dot-com collapses. Known for his owl-like, oversize glasses, Greenspan could be considered the world's first celebrity economist. People waited on his every word, eager to see how his economic proclamations and predictions would direct the daily market. While he did fail to foresee the credit bubble that nearly broke down the financial system after he left the Fed, he also managed to guide the country through one of the longest economic booms in history.

28. Besides being CEO of Starbucks, Howard Schultz also is known for what?

a. Owning the Denver Nuggets
b. Owning the Chicago Bulls
c. Owning the New York Knicks
d. Owning the Seattle Supersonics

29. Leonard Samuel Shoen founded U-Haul with an investment of how much money?

a. $5,000
b. $15,000
c. $1,500
d. $50

30. What was Andrew Grove, Intel's CEO, childhood name?

a. Intel
b. Andris
c. Andy
d. He didn't have one

31. Who is chairman and CEO of Goldman Sachs?

a. Sandy Weill
b. Lloyd Blankfein
c. Michael Steinhardt
d. Robert Rubin

32. Who is the former CEO of The Walt Disney Company?

a. Herbert Allen
b. David Geffen
c. Michael Eisner
d. Jeffrey Katzenberg

33. What did Mark Zuckerberg launch from his Harvard dorm room on February 4, 2004?

a. Facebook
b. Google
c. Twitter
d. YouTube

34. Who is considered the pioneer of the "warehouse store" retail model?

a. Sol Price
b. Julius Rosenwald
c. Bernard Marcus
d. Gerald Levin

35. What was the name of the course Asher Edelman—whom *Wall Street*'s Gordon Gekko was based on—taught at Columbia Business School?

a. "The Five Dysfunctions of a Team"
b. "Cut-throat Capitalism"
c. "Lunch Is for Wimps"
d. "Corporate Raiding—The Art of War"

36. What did Marc Rich receive from President Bill Clinton on Clinton's last day in office?

a. A phone call
b. The President's Award
c. A presidential pardon
d. The Excel Award

37. What school did Sandy Weill, former CEO and chairman of Citigroup, attend in Brooklyn, New York?

a. P.S. 200
b. Brooklyn Technical High School
c. Edward R. Murrow High School
d. Pratt Institute

38. What are the two Las Vegas casinos that Sheldon Adelson owns?

a. Bellagio and Hard Rock Hotel
b. Venetian and Sands
c. Bellagio and Venetian
d. Flamingo and Sands

39. Who is chairman and CEO of IAC/InterActiveCorp?

a. Herbert Allen
b. Edgar Bronfman
c. Barry Diller
d. Michael Ovitz

40. Which of the following films did Jeffrey Katzenberg *not* produce through DreamWorks Animation?

a. *Shrek*
b. *The Prince of Egypt*
c. *Over the Hedge*
d. *The Little Mermaid*

41. What former department store was started by a Bavarian Jewish immigrant and was known for creating the oldest Thanksgiving Day parade in the country?

a. Gimbel's
b. Macy's
c. Bloomingdale's
d. Nordstrom

42. Samuel Irving Newhouse is the chairman and CEO of Advance Publications, which owns what?

a. Hearst
b. Disney
c. Miramax
d. Conde Nast

43. What did Eugene Mayer purchase at a bankruptcy auction in the Great Depression?

a. *The Washington Post*
b. *The New York Times*
c. *New York Sun*
d. *The Wall Street Journal*

44. Leonard Stern, the billionaire owner of the Hartz Mountain pet products company, owned what New York City paper until 2000?

a. *New York Post*
b. *The Village Voice*
c. *Newsday*
d. *New York Sun*

45. Mortimer Zuckerman is the publisher and owner of which newspaper?

a. *Chicago Tribune*
b. *The Boston Globe*
c. *New York Daily News*
d. *Las Vegas Sun*

46. **What happened to Ben Bernanke, current chairman of the Federal Reserve System, in 2009?**

a. *Time* magazine named him "Person of the Year"
b. He was acquitted of fraud
c. He was married
d. He received an honorary degree from Columbia Business School

47. **What was Jacob Mincer's contribution to economic science?**

a. He developed the concept of free market enterprise
b. He helped develop the empirical foundations of the human capital theory
c. He developed the system of supply and demand
d. He developed the economic shock theory

48. **What was Ivan Boesky best known for in the late 1980s and early '90s?**

a. Founding Marshall Field's
b. His philanthropic work
c. A Wall Street insider trading scandal
d. His massive art collection

49. **What size donation did Bruce Wasserstein give to Harvard Law School?**

a. $10 million
b. $15 million
c. $20 million
d. $25 million

50. Which Jewish gangster helped build Las Vegas?

a. Bugsy Siegel
b. Meyer Lansky
c. Longy Zwillman
d. Moe Dalitz

CHAPTER EIGHT

Schmatte Chic: Fashion

"Clothes don't make the man, but clothes have got many a man a good job."—Michael Kors

The history of Jews in fashion can be summed up in few words: from ghetto to glamour. In Europe, few professions were open to Jews. Largely barred from owning land, they often made do as tailors, honing skills that would translate well in the New World. In the nineteenth century, the sewing machine revolutionized the apparel business, and Jewish immigrants were the backbone of garment factories in New York and other big cities. Valerie Steele, director and chief curator at the Fashion Institute of Technology, explains, "Based in urban centers and pushed by history toward entrepreneurship, Jews found fashion as one of the fields open to them." Today, they are a dominant force in the industry—from ghetto to glamour indeed!

1. How many Academy Awards did American costume designer Edith Head win?

    a. 8
    b. 9
    c. 10
    d. 15

2. Diane von Furstenberg is most famous for what iconic piece of clothing?

    a. The bikini
    b. The bra
    c. The wrap dress
    d. The apron

3. Which film did Adrian (Adrian Adolph Greenburg) design the costumes for?

    a. *King Kong*
    b. *Sabrina*
    c. *The Wizard of Oz*
    d. *Mutiny on the Bounty*

4. Who said, "I don't design clothes. I design dreams"?

    a. Ralph Lauren
    b. Donna Karen
    c. Zac Posen
    d. Michael Kors

5. In 2001, Alber Elbaz was appointed artistic director of which company?

a. Yves Saint Laurent
b. Lanvin
c. Chanel
d. Christian Dior

6. Which fashion designer was named to *Time* magazine's "World's Most Influential People" for 2010?

a. Alexandre Herchcovitch
b. Richard Blackwell
c. Max Azria
d. Marc Jacobs

7. Which designer was once described by the *New York Times* as "[Ed Koch] in a stretchy black dress"?

a. Diane von Furstenberg
b. Anne Klein
c. Donna Karan
d. Monica Lewinsky

8. Which fashion designer is one of the regular judges on TV's reality show *Project Runway*?

a. Isaac Mizrahi
b. Calvin Klein
c. Zac Posen
d. Michael Kors

9. **According to legend, what shop did Calvin Klein found in 1968 in New York City's York Hotel with $10,000?**

   a. Calvin Klein Limited, a coat shop
   b. Calvin Klein Shoes
   c. Calvin Klein Exchange, a hat shop
   d. CK, a suit emporium

10. **Which fashion designer made a guest appearance on TV's *Ugly Betty* in an episode called "Lose the Boss"?**

   a. Ralph Lauren
   b. Sonia Rykiel
   c. Marc Ecko
   d. Isaac Mizrahi

11. **What year was Zac Posen born?**

   a. 1960
   b. 1970
   c. 1976
   d. 1980

12. **Which designer is nicknamed the "Queen of Knits"?**

   a. Anne Klein
   b. Sonia Rykiel
   c. Charlotte Ronson
   d. Judith Leiber

13. **What is Ralph Lauren's birth name?**

   a. Ralph Lifshitz
   b. Ralph Greenberg
   c. Ralph Isaacs
   d. Ralph Elie Tahari

14. **What document was Nicole Farhi a signatory to in 2007?**

a. Nuclear Non-Proliferation Treaty

b. Independent Jewish Voices

c. An open letter to Israel from *The New York Times*

d. The Council of Fashion Designers of America's letter to President George Bush

15. **What is Marc Ecko's alma mater?**

a. Yale

b. Harvard

c. Rutgers

d. New York University

16. **What is Elie Tahari's birth city?**

a. New York City

b. Huntington (Long Island), New York

c. Jerusalem

d. Athens

17. **What is Max Azria's fashion line, BCBGMAXAZRIA, named after?**

a. His mother's initials, followed by his name

b. His father's initials, followed by his name

c. The French phrase *bon chic, bon genre*, followed by his name

d. The phrase "before Christ, before God," followed by his name

18. Who crafted the first pair of riveted jeans—made with material from the Levi Strauss general store in San Francisco—and arranged for their patent in 1873?

a. Jacob Davis
b. David Jacobs
c. Mark Jacobs
d. Jacob Isaacs

19. What was Levi Strauss's birth name?

a. Josh Strauss
b. Loeb Strauss
c. Ralph Strauss
d. Max Strauss

20. What shirt-making company became the first to advertise in *The Saturday Evening Post*?

a. David Strauss and Co.
b. Levi 501
c. M. Phillips & Son
d. Adrian & Sons

21. Who is the founder of Link Theory and an investor in Helmut Lang?

a. Judith Leiber
b. Henri Willis Bendel
c. Rudi Gernreich
d. Andrew Rosen

22. **Who dressed Joan Crawford, Tallulah Bankhead, Clare Booth Luce, and the Duchess of Windsor?**

a. Hattie Carnegie
b. Adrian
c. Sally Milgrim
d. Nettie Rosenstein

23. **Who designed Eleanor Roosevelt's inaugural ball dress in 1933?**

a. Nettie Rosenstein
b. Inga Nataya
c. Sally Milgrim
d. Adrian

24. **What was the famous Calvin Klein tagline for a 1980 provocative ad that featured 15-year-old Brooke Shields?**

a. "My bottoms are tops."
b. "Made for pleasure."
c. "The perfect jeans."
d. "Do you want to know what comes between me and my Calvins? Nothing."

25. **Without funds to rent a hotel room, let alone a showroom, for his shoe designs, Kenneth Cole rented a trailer. Because New York City only would grant trailer permits to movie companies, Cole changed his company name to what?**

a. Kenneth Cole Productions
b. Kenneth Cole Catering
c. Kenneth Cole Films
d. Kenneth Cole Trailers

26. Who is credited with creating the first monokini?

   a. Diane von Furstenberg
   b. Michael Kors
   c. Rudi Gernreich
   d. Max Azria

27. Ida Rosenthal and her husband created what company?

   a. Bloomingdale's
   b. Maidenform
   c. Neiman-Marcus
   d. Saks Fifth Avenue

28. Henri Willis Bendel, founder of the upscale women's fashion store that bears his name, was the first retailer to bring whose designs to the United States?

   a. Yves Saint Laurent
   b. Christian Dior
   c. Vivienne Westwood
   d. Coco Chanel

29. Nudie Cohn created suits for celebrities such as Elvis Presley, Roy Rogers, and Gram Parsons. What type of suits is he most famous for designing?

   a. Rhinestone-encrusted suits
   b. Track suits
   c. Sweat suits
   d. Tuxedos

30. **Who was the first woman to join the handbag-makers guild in Budapest?**

    a. Susan Matheson
    b. Charlotte Ronson
    c. Judith Leiber
    d. Betsey Johnson

31. **Who is the CEO of American Apparel, as well as the nephew of noted architect Moshe Safdie?**

    a. Dov Charney
    b. Richard Blackwell
    c. Marc Ecko
    d. Alber Elbaz

32. **Where are Elena Benarroch's designs most popular?**

    a. England
    b. France
    c. Spain
    d. Italy

33. **What company did Lena Himmelstein found?**

    a. Dress Barn
    b. Banana Republic
    c. Juicy
    d. Lane Bryant

34. **Michele Bohbot is the designer for which leading JC Penney brand?**

    a. Bisou Bisou
    b. MNG by Mango
    c. Uproar
    d. Aldo

35. **What is fashion critic Richard Blackwell known for creating?**

a. The "Fifty Best Dressed Women List"
b. The Academy Award Fashion List
c. The "Ten Worst Dressed Women List"
d. The "Ten Best Designers List"

The "Wrap Dress"

✡

In 1976, Diana Vreeland, editor of *Vogue*, showcased Diane von Furstenberg's wrap dress in the pages her magazine, and working women across America rejoiced. Finally! An affordable dress that, with one tug of its slinky sash, could go from boardroom to *boudoir*. Later that same year, *Newsweek* proclaimed Furstenberg as "the most marketable female in fashion since Coco Chanel." A symbol of sexual liberation, the body-hugging dress is so emblematic that it hangs in the Smithsonian Institute. And what about Furstenberg? As of 2009, she is still championing women's success—her $200 million-plus company is staffed by 155 employees, 97 percent of whom are women. And to think a little dress started it all.

36. Brazilian designer Alexandre Herchovitch is known for what kind of designs?

a. Avante-garde
b. Minimalist
c. Asian-influenced
d. Draping

37. Who was the first Jewish designer to have his work featured on the holiday cover of *Vogue*?

a. Ralph Lauren
b. Scaasi
c. Calvin Klein
d. Michael Kors

38. Who was featured in a Gap ad with a Star of David necklace provocatively clenched between his teeth?

a. Jon Stewart
b. David Spade
c. Jeremy Piven
d. Shia LaBeouf

39. Whose photography career is depicted fictitiously in the film *Funny Face*?

a. Richard Avedon
b. Robert Capa
c. Robert Frank
d. Weegee

40. Dora Kallmus worked with Josephine Baker, Colette, and Maurice Chevalier, among others. What was her profession?

a. Stylist
b. Fashion and portrait photographer
c. Model
d. Hat designer

41. Who has a work of photography titled *The Ballad of Sexual Dependency*?

a. Cindy Sherman
b. Helen Levitt
c. Nan Goldin
d. Diane Arbus

42. Annie Leibovitz, known for her portraiture work, took a picture of which celebrity bathing in milk?

a. Whoopi Goldberg
b. Demi Moore
c. Yoko Ono
d. Miley Cyrus

43. Which photographer is well known for taking photos of herself dressed in costumes?

a. Diane Arbus
b. Nan Goldin
c. Helen Levitt
d. Cindy Sherman

44. Which model is known both for her 2009 cover of the *Sports Illustrated* swimsuit issue and for dating actor Leonardo DiCaprio?

a. Bar Refaeli
b. Brooklyn Decker
c. Marisa Miller
d. Rachel Hunter

45. What did *Heeb* magazine publish for the first time in 2008?

a. A list of the best Jewish fashion designers
b. The "Ten Best-Dressed Jews List"
c. The first Jewish swimsuit calendar
d. The "Ten Worst-Dress Jews List"

46. Who is Hannah Golofski?

a. Charlotte Ronson
b. Nicole Farhi
c. Anne Klein
d. Edith Head

47. Who did Yotam Solomon dress for her premiere on TV's *Dancing with the Stars*?

a. Natalie Coughlin
b. Kate Gosselin
c. Pamela Anderson
d. Nicole Scherzinger

48. Who said, "You can have anything you want in life if you dress for it"?

  a. Edith Head
  b. Calvin Klein
  c. Scaasi
  d. Ralph Lauren

49. Who reportedly pawned his wife's engagement ring to pay for rent and an inventory of 40 men's suits so he could open a discount store?

  a. Marcus Pressman
  b. Neiman Marcus
  c. Barney Pressman
  d. Barney Marcus

50. Which designer incorporates socially aware statements into his campaign slogans?

  a. Calvin Klein
  b. Ralph Lauren
  c. Marc Jacobs
  d. Kenneth Cole

CHAPTER NINE

Who Said That?: Famous Quotes

Jews are a group of famously funny, witty, and insightful people. Don't believe me? Read for yourself . . .

Match the quote with the person who said it on page 132.

1. "Despite everything, I believe that people are really good at heart."

2. "If God wanted us to fly, he would have given us tickets."

3. "People first, then money, then things."

4. "Attitude is everything."

5. "Life is divided into the horrible and the miserable."

6. "Age is strictly a case of mind over matter. If you don't mind, it doesn't matter."

7. "If opportunity doesn't knock, build a door."

8. "Insomnia is my greatest inspiration."

9. "I never know how much of what I say is true."

10. "New York is not Mecca. It just smells like it."

11. "A bookstore is one of the only pieces of evidence we have that people are still thinking."

12. "I dream for a living."

13. "A song is anything that can walk by itself."

14. "It is every woman's dream to be some man's dream woman."

15. "I think of my body as a side effect of my mind."

16. "Gentlemen, start your egos."

17. "If you don't risk anything, you risk even more."

18. "Your dresses should be tight enough to show you're a woman and loose enough to show you're a lady."

19. "Hey, I may loathe myself, but it has nothing to do with the fact that I'm Jewish."

20. "I'm Jewish, but I'm totally not."

21. "Communism is like one big phone company."

22. "A man is only as good as what he loves."

23. "Creationists make it sound as though a theory is something you dreamt up after being drunk all night."

24. "From each according to his abilities, to each according to his needs."

25. "You cannot simultaneously prevent and prepare for war."

26. "I should warn you: If I turn out to be particularly clear, you've probably misunderstood what I've said."

27. "You can't put your feet on the ground until you've touched the sky."

28. "Never go for the punch line. There might be something funnier on the way."

29. "Everybody ought to have a Lower East Side in their life."

30. "Songs are life in 80 words or less."

31. "Misfits aren't misfits among other misfits."

32. "The Republicans are the party of bad ideas. The Democrats are the party of no ideas."

33. "I've had great success being a total idiot."

34. "It's easier to put on slippers than to carpet the whole world."

35. "Anatomy is destiny."

36. "Both the man of science and the man of action live always at the edge of mystery, surrounded by it."

37. "Einstein, stop telling God what to do!"

38. "Accent your positive and delete your negative."

39. "Life is a lot like jazz…it's best when you improvise."

40. "Google's not a real company."

41. "Life improves slowly and goes wrong fast, and only catastrophe is clearly visible."

42. "My strength is coming up with two outs in the last of the ninth."

43. "You can only work for people you like."

44. "Colorless green ideas sleep furiously."

45. "Some men are born mediocre, some men achieve mediocrity, and some men have mediocrity thrust upon them."

46. "America, I've given you all, and now I'm nothing."

47. "I've never been a millionaire, but I know I'd be darling at it."

48. "If you ever forget you're a Jew, a Gentile will remind you."

49. "Alimony is the curse of the writing class."

50. "To be a Jew is a destiny."

Woody Allen

Isaac Asimov

Paul Auster

Steve Ballmer

Vicki Baum

Saul Bellow

Jack Benny

Milton Berle

Irving Berlin

Lewis Black

Niels Bohr

Mel Brooks

Lenny Bruce

Noam Chomsky

Billy Crystal

Larry David

Neil Diamond

Bob Dylan

Michael Eisner

Albert Einstein

Carrie Fisher

Anne Frank

Al Franken

Sigmund Freud

George Gershwin

Allen Ginsberg

Milton Glaser

Alan Greenspan

Edith Head

Joseph Heller

Erica Jong

Donna Karan

Jerry Lewis

Norman Mailer

Bernard Malamud

Barry Manilow

Karl Marx

Bette Midler

J. Robert Oppenheimer

Suze Orman

Dorothy Parker

Philip Roth

Jerry Seinfeld

Sarah Silverman

Neil Simon

Steven Spielberg

Barbra Streisand

Jon Stewart

Jerry Stiller

Edward Teller

Diane von Furstenberg

Answers

Chapter One

The Good Old Days: Jewish and Israeli History

1. d. He fled the City of Ur and crossed the River Eber
2. b. A covenant with God; many of his descendants henceforth would be known as Hebrews.
3. a. Ishmael
4. a. Esau
5. c. Israel, which means "fighter for God"
6. d. The Israelites
7. a. Judah, one of the twelve sons of Jacob
8. b. The first Prime Minister of Israel
9. c. Someone who is born and/or lives in Israel
10. c. The Promised Land
11. d. The United States
12. b. Ground, or earth
13. a. The first chief rabbi of Israel
14. c. Statues of local deities, found in homes during the Bronze Age
15. d. 1948
16. a. 1948
17. b. Monotheism
18. b. A ram
19. d. Adam and Eve, Abraham and Sarah, Isaac and Rebekah, and Jacob and Leah
20. a. Since she died giving birth, she has a tomb of her own so she can pray for her children as they pass her on their way to exile.
21. c. Nahum Sokolow
22. a. The Ten Commandments
23. b. Michelangelo
24. d. Monotheism
25. d. Drawn (drawn out). "And she named him Moses, and said, 'Because I drew him out of the water.'" (Exodus 2:10)
26. c. "Let my people go."
27. a. Blood, frogs, lice, wild animals, plague, boils, hail, locusts, darkness, and death of the firstborn
28. a. Its exact location is unknown
29. b. "I am the Lord thy God"
30. d. A person's duties regarding his relationship to God
31. a. The relationship of man to his fellow man
32. c. 613
33. c. ...who will be for me?"
34. a. 40 years
35. d. Moses lived to that age
36. c. The sound of the *shofar*, the ram's horn
37. a. They held a lottery

38. a. Deborah

39. b. A *shtarker* (a strong and brave person)

40. d. A donkey's jawbone

41. a. He lost his power, was blinded by the Philistines, then was taken prisoner

42. d. "Let me die with the Philistines!"

43. a. David

44. c. Bathsheba

45. c. His hair became entangled in the braches of a tree, leaving him hanging there to be stabbed to death

46. a. In the valley of Kidron

47. d. It has only seven branches

48. c. Holy of Holies

49. a. Limestone

50. a. Assyria

51. d. Jezebel

52. c. A pagan temple

53. a. Elijah

54. a. The Babylonians

55. b. *Shul*

56. c. Priest

57. c. The YMCA

58. d. Five: the Song of Songs, Book of Ruth, Lamentations, Ecclesiastes, and Book of Esther

59. a. He died, 120 years later

60. a. By number, except for Shabbat: Sunday is the first day; Monday is the second day, etc.

61. c. Netanya

62. c. The Trans-Israel Highway

63. a. Masada, a fortress built by King Herod around 40 BCE

64. d. Kibbutz *Lohamei Hageta'ot*

65. b. A collective community in Israel

66. c. Charleston, S.C.

67. a. 1967

68. c. 80%

69. c. House Minority Whip

70. a. Christopher Columbus's interpreter, Luis de Torres

71. c. They are all astronauts

72. a. The lynching of Leo Frank

73. d. 1984

74. a. The journey of 8,000 Ethiopian Jews through Sudan to Israel

75. b. Marranos. However, because Jews never used that term (in Spanish, it means "pigs"), they referred to them as *anusim*: "those who were forced to convert."

Chapter Two
L' Chaim: Holidays

1. c. On the fourteenth day of the Hebrew month of *Adar*

2. d. Book of Esther

3. b. Dancing with friends

4. a. Yiddish theater

5. a. Nuts

6. d. Wine

7. c. *Hamantaschen,* triangle-shaped cookies

8. a. Her Jewish identity

9. d. 13

10. a. Passover

11. a. The fact that God "passed over" the houses of the Jews when He was slaying the firstborn of Egypt

12. d. Leavened bread, to recognize that the Hebrews fled Egypt in such a hurry that they did not have time to let their bread rise.

13. b. The *afikomen,* or dessert matzoh

14. b. Jethro (Yitro)

15. a. Weeks (*Shavout* is the Festival of Weeks)

16. c. 7 days; 8 days outside of Israel

17. a. Caramel

18. d. A song sung during Passover

19. c. The dedication at the beginning of the evening service on *Yom Kippur*

20. a. 25 hours

21. a. No laughing or crying

22. c. The miraculous burning of oil for eight days

23. b. Lights

24. d. Antiochus

25. d. The Maccabees

26. a. Oily (fried) food

27. c. Small amounts of money, the traditional gift of *Hanukkah*

28. d. A spinning top marked with four Hebrew letters and traditionally played during *Hanukkah*

29. a. Some

30. c. *Rosh Hashanah*

31. a. On *Shavuot*, Jews read a Torah portion that includes the Ten Commandments

32. b. Honey

33. c. "For a good year!"

34. c. During the ten days from the beginning of *Rosh Hashanah* to the end of *Yom Kippur*

35. d. *Sukkot*

36. a. The age of a recently planted tree

37. c. Branches of trees, known collectively as the *lulav*

38. a. Guests; more specifically, the seven notable "guests" (Abraham, Isaac, Jacob, Moses, Aaron, Joseph, and David) who are symbolically welcomed into the *sukkah*.

39. d. Dipping eggs into salt water

40. a. *Neilah*

41. b. ...the Sabbath has kept the Jews." Essayist Ahad Ha'am (1856–1927) first said this.

42. d. From sundown Friday until sundown on Saturday

43. a. The Ten Commandments

44. b. Lighting of the candles

45. c. Nepal

46. b. Abraham Lincoln

47. d. 1837

48. c. Chocolate

49. d. A New York-based association of hard-core *dreidel* enthusiasts

50. c. *Latkes* (potato pancakes)

Chapter Three
And All That Jazz: Entertainment

1. d. Marvin Hamlisch

2. c. The raving Absalom

3. a. Irving Berlin

4. a. Universal Pictures

5. c. Paramount Pictures

6. d. Fox Film Corporation

7. c. Metro-Goldwyn-Mayer

8. c. Warner Bros.

9. a. Woody Allen

10. c. Kirk Douglas

11. a. Lauren Bacall

12. d. a Passover seder with Zeppo Marx (a distant cousin of Sadye's)

13. a. Groucho Marx

14. d. Milton Berle

15. a. Marc Chagall

16. d. The Statue of Liberty

17. c. Harry Houdini

18. b. Florenz (Flo) Ziegfield

19. a. *Hanukkah*

20. b. Violin

21. b. *The Odd Couple*

22. c. Bentz and Arik

23. a. 5

24. b. A rabbi

25. c. When they find our Jerry made out during *Schindler's List*

26. c. Jon Stewart

27. d. Larry David

28. b. DreamWorks

29. a. Mike Nichols

30. c. 5

31. a. The Department of Psychiatry and Neurology at Valley Forge General Hospital in Phoenixville, Penn.

32. c. Chicken soup

33. c. Chief prosecutor of the Austrian Empire

34. c. Mike Wallace

35. b. 1989

36. c. Professor

37. b. Billie Holiday

38. a. Dan Aykroyd

39. b. Mel Brooks

40. c. Tony Curtis

41. a. Sarah Silverman

42. d. Dustin Hoffman

43. b. Julius, Arthur, and Leonard

44. a. Joel Grey

45. a. "A Yiddishe Mamme"

46. b. The Catskills. The term was coined in the 1920s to describe the resort area of New York State's southern Catskill Mountains, a training ground for Jewish performers.

47. a. *The King of Comedy*

48. d. 1974

49. b. Green-Wood Cemetery in Brooklyn

50. b. Benny Goodman

51. c. *The New York Times*

52. c. Joseph Pulitzer

53. a. The Columbia School of Journalism. He donated money in 1903, but the school didn't open with its first classes until 1912.

54. b. A Jewish magazine aimed at young, hip adults

55. b. *Forward*

56. c. Shalom Aleichem

57. d. *Tevye the Dairyman*, which became the basis for *Fiddler on the Roof*

58. a. Salo W. Baron

59. c. *Goodbye, Columbus*

60. a. The Nobel Prize for Literature

61. d. *Fear of Flying*

62. a. *Catch-22*, by Joseph Heller

63. c. Dorothy Parker

64. c. "I saw the best minds of my generation destroyed by madness, starving hysterical naked…"

65. d. Maurice Sendak

66. a. Peter Max

67. b. James Baldwin

68. a. *Vogue*

69. c. His personal art collection. At the time, it was the largest single bequest ever received by the museum.

70. c. Modern

71. d. Alfred Stieglitz, the famous photographer

72. a. Norman Mailer

73. a. His son, Abraham Isaac Wouk, who died in a tragic accident as a small child

74. c. Reuven Malter

75. a. A sewing machine

Chapter Four
We Are the Champions: Sports

1. c. Sandy Koufax. He was inducted in 1972, when he was only 37 years old.

2. d. Won seven gold medals at the Munich Olympics, a record that wasn't broken until 2008 by Michael Phelps

3. b. Johnny Kling

4. b. Dolph Schayes

5. c. Hank Greenberg, in 1956

6. a. Ron Bloomberg

7. d. Mike Rossman

8. c. Sid Luckman

9. a. 11

10. c. Tal Brody

11. a. Benny Leonard

12. c. Bill Goldberg

13. a. She won 10 medals in 3 Olympiads, all in gymnastics

14. d. Sidney Franklin

15. b. Princeton

16. c. Syd Cohen

17. a. "The Yiddish Curver." Pelty often was erroneously referred to as Peltheimer.

18. d. Garry Kimovich Kasparov retired

19. b. Deep Blue, a computer developed by IBM

20. a. Michael Thaler

21. b. He has a fierce, predatory style in the box

22. d. One of Maccabi Tel Aviv's greatest soccer players

23. a. He is the all-time leading Jewish scorer in NHL history.

24. b. Created the Boston Celtics dynasty that won nine NBA championships (eight of them consecutive) over ten years

25. c. Yuri Foreman, who was born in Belarus and trained in Brooklyn

26. d. Allen Davis, the pro football Hall of Famer who is president and principal owner of the Oakland Raiders.

27. b. Russian, English, and Hebrew

28. a. He competed in six consecutive Olympiads for the U.S. equestrian team, the most ever for an American dressage rider.

29. a. Sergei Charikov

30. b. They were the first American team in Olympic history to capture a gold medal in whitewater slalom

31. a. Shooting

32. b. Agneshka Brustman

33. c. Kailua, Hawaii

34. c. He became the youngest U.S. black belt at the Japan Karate Association

35. a. A left-footed punter for the Tennessee Titans

36. d. The 2003 World Women's Mistral Championship title in Spain; Korsitz was only 19 at the time.

37. b. She was injured during her service in the Israel Defense Forces, while training to be an officer

38. c. Max Birbraer

39. d. When he made a goal, he celebrated his victory by mimicking an airplane

40. a. Eli Ohana

41. c. *Time*

42. b. Jonathan Erlich

43. c. The Washington Wizards

44. d. Doron Sheffer, an Israeli basketball player

45. a. He never fought professionally again

46. d. All of this above; he is a practicing Orthodox Jew.

47. a. Dick Savitt; he is a member of the International Tennis Hall of Fame and is the only Jew to win the Wimbledon singles championship. (Boris Becker did not identify himself as a Jew when he won.)

48. b. Chess

49. c. Henry Wittenberg; he won more than 300 consecutive matches between 1939 and 1951.

50. a. Ken Holtzman

Chapter Five
But Is It Kosher?: Food

1. a. Grilled food
2. d. Iraq
3. a. The law of keeping food kosher
4. c. Meat and dairy
5. b. Blood
6. b. Manischewitz
7. a. Labrusca grapes
8. a. The number of seeds in the fruit—613—corresponds to the number of *mitzvot* (rules) in the Torah
9. d. Ashes
10. d. Heavy sour cream
11. a. It contains neither dairy nor meat products
12. a. Bagel
13. c. The portion of dough set aside for the *kohen*
14. a. Chicken soup
15. d. Knish
16. c. Cholent
17. a. Orange, because it is made with carrots
18. a. A big fuss
19. b. Russ & Daughters
20. a. Bialys. The name of the book was *The Bialy Eaters: The Story of a Bread and a Lost World.*
21. d. ...runneth over."
22. d. Buckwheat and bowtie pasta
23. a. *Sufganiyot*
24. d. Forbidden, or *trayf*
25. a. To slaughter all meat and poultry for kosher consumption
26. d. The lungs
27. c. Fins and overlapping scales that can be removed while leaving the skin intact
28. d. Barley, wheat, figs, dates, pomegranates, olives, and grapes
29. c. Before food; an appetizer
30. c. He opened New York City's Stage Deli
31. d. Barney Greengrass
32. d. Passover scrambled eggs
33. d. Katz's Deli
34. a. Essex Street to Orchard Street
35. a. H&H Bagels
36. a. To put a celebrity sandwich on the menu. These creations continue today, such as the Dolly Parton (pastrami and corned beef on twin rolls) and the Kevin Bacon, Lettuce and Tomato.
37. d. Corned Beef Row
38. b. Nate 'n Al Delicatessen
39. c. They lost their original Jersey deli in the 1929 stock market crash and looked to California for better fortunes
40. a. Milton Berle
41. d. Paprika-dusted, twice-smoked slices of pickled fat from a brisket
42. c. Sweet raisin sauce
43. a. Seltzer
44. b. nosher
45. a. Dr. Brown's Cel-Ray Soda
46. b. Egg Cream, which contains chocolate syrup, milk, and seltzer water
47. c. Schmear
48. a. He hosted an art show called "Man and Liver" for which various artists created sculptures out of the food
49. a. Smoked salmon
50. b. The founder, Abe Lebewohl, was killed during a robbery in 1996

Chapter Six
It's All Relative: Science and Medicine

1. a. Novocain
2. c. Wolfgang Pauli
3. b. Karl Koller
4. a. Neurons
5. a. Albert Einstein
6. c. 1982
7. b. Uranus
8. d. Superstring theory; he actually campaigned to keep string theorists out of Harvard. When the physics department embraced the theory, he left.
9. a. David Gestetner
10. c. 1915
11. b. J. Robert Oppenheimer
12. a. Jonas Salk
13. d. 1935
14. a. Carl Sagan
15. b. Roald Hoffman
16. d. Moritz Kaposi
17. b. Itzhak Bentov
18. d. The Nobel Prizes won by Max von Laue and James Franck; he dissolved the gold awards with aqua regia. After the war, the Nobel Society recast the awards using the original gold.
19. a. Leslie Brent
20. c. Jacob Bronowski
21. a. Architecture
22. d. Albert Sabin
23. b. Albert Abraham Michelson
24. a. 15
25. a. The first nuclear explosion at Alamagordo on July 16, 1945
26. c. He was involved in a streetcar accident as a child and was forced to wear a prosthetic foot, which gave him a life-long limp.
27. b. Saul Amarel
28. a. Dogs, 78 beagles to be precise, via tracheotomies
29. d. Albert Einstein
30. b. Aaron Temkin Beck
31. a. Leptin
32. b. A nuclear submarine
33. a. The genetic code
34. a. Meyer R. Schkolnick
35. c. Lise Meitner
36. b. Richard Lewontin
37. c. Edwin H. Land
38. a. Hepatitis B
39. d. Claude Levi-Strauss
40. b. Esther Lederberg
41. c. Sigmund Freud
42. a. Simon Baruch
43. d. A fire destroyed it, along with all of his personal notes and letters
44. a. Hermann Bondi
45. d. Paul Nemenyi
46. c. Obedience; the studies proved how easily human beings can hurt one another when given the authority to do so.
47. b. Direct microbiological observations
48. b. Phoebus Levene
49. d. Karl Landsteiner
50. c. Eugen Glueckauf

Chapter Seven
If I Were a Rich Man: Business

1. c. Harry Markowitz
2. b. Max Levchin, c. Luke Nosek, and d. Ken Howery; they were all co-founders

3. d. Kenneth Arrow

4. a. Michael Bloomberg

5. b. The free market economy

6. c. *Security Analysis*

7. d. 1987–2006

8. a. He gave the keynote address at the Consumer Electronics Show because Bill Gates, who usually handled the keynote, left Microsoft as full-time chairman.

9. c. Google

10. b. Clive Davis

11. a. A major enterprise software company

12. b. An American casino resort/real estate developer, better known as Steve Wynn

13. d. Equity Group Investments

14. a. He is an owner of the Saatchi Gallery and is known for his sponsorship of the Young British Artists, including Damien Hirst.

15. b. eBay

16. a. His philanthropic efforts

17. b. 27

18. c. Bernard Madoff

19. b. Michael Milken

20. d. Suze Orman

21. a. Richard Pratt, who was known as the "Cardboard King" because of his cardboard box company and the cardboard cartel he ran.

22. b. The "Man Who Broke the Bank of England"

23. b. Sumner Redstone

24. c. Sears, Roebuck and Company

25. d. Bernie Marcus

26. a. Picasso's *Nude on a Black Armchair*

27. a. Wards, founded in 1949 by Samuel Wurtzel

28. d. Owning the Seattle Supersonics

29. a. $5,000

30. b. Andris

31. b. Lloyd Blankfein

32. c. Michael Eisner

33. a. Facebook

34. a. Sol Price, founder of Price Club and Fed Mart (Price Club later merged with Costco.)

35. d. "Corporate Raiding—The Art of War"

36. c. A presidential pardon

37. a. P.S. 200

38. b. Venetian and Sands

39. c. Barry Diller

40. d. *The Little Mermaid*

41. a. Gimbel's, started by Adam Gimbel

42. d. Conde Nast

43. a. *The Washington Post*

44. b. *The Village Voice*

45. c. *New York Daily News*

46. a. *Time* magazine named him "Person of the Year"

47. b. He helped develop the empirical foundations of the human capital theory

48. c. A Wall Street insider trading scandal

49. d. $25 million

50. a. Bugsy Siegel

Chapter Eight
Schmatte Chic: Fashion

1. a. 8, the most awards the Academy had given to a woman

2. c. The wrap dress

3. c. *The Wizard of Oz*

4. a. Ralph Lauren

5. b. Lanvin

6. d. Marc Jacobs

7. c. Donna Karan

8. d. Michael Kors

9. a. Calvin Klein Limited, a coat shop

10. d. Isaac Mizrahi

11. d. 1980

12. b. Sonia Rykiel

13. a. Ralph Lifshitz

14. b. Independent Jewish Voices, a Jewish network that calls for an open debate on Israel

15. c. Rutgers

16. c. Jerusalem

17. c. The French phrase *bon chic, bon genre*, followed by his name

18. a. Jacob Davis

19. b. Loeb Strauss

20. c. M. Phillips & Son

21. d. Andrew Rosen

22. a. Hattie Carnegie

23. c. Sally Milgrim

24. d. "Do you want to know what comes between me and my Calvins? Nothing."

25. a. Kenneth Cole Productions

26. c. Rudi Gernreich

27. b. Maidenform

28. d. Coco Chanel

29. a. Rhinestone-encrusted suits

30. c. Judith Leiber

31. a. Dov Charney

32. c. Spain

33. d. Lane Bryant; Bryant was her married name, and "Lane" came from a banker's misspelling on a business account application.

34. a. Bisou Bisou

35. c. The "Ten Worst Dressed Women List"

36. a. Avante-garde

37. b. Scassi, originally known as Arnold Isaacs (He reversed the letters of his last name.)

38. c. Jeremy Piven

39. a. Richard Avedon

40. b. Fashion and portrait photographer

41. c. Nan Goldin

42. a. Whoopi Goldberg

43. d. Cindy Sherman

44. a. Bar Refaeli

45. c. The first Jewish swimsuit calendar, titled "The Ladies of '69," a reference to the Hebrew year of 5769

46. c. Anne Klein

47. a. Natalie Coughlin

48. a. Edith Head

49. c. Barney Pressman

50. d. Kenneth Cole; his was the first fashion company to take a stand against AIDS.

Chapter Nine
Who Said That?: Famous Quotes

1. "Despite everything, I believe that people are really good at heart." —Anne Frank

2. "If God wanted us to fly, he would have given us tickets." —Mel Brooks

3. "People first, then money, then things." —Suze Orman

4. "Attitude is everything." —Diane von Furstenberg

5. "Life is divided into the horrible and the miserable." —Woody Allen

6. "Age is strictly a case of mind over matter. If you don't mind, it doesn't matter." —Jack Benny

7. "If opportunity doesn't knock, build a door." —Milton Berle

8. "Insomnia is my greatest inspiration." —Jon Stewart

9. "I never know how much of what I say is true." —Bette Midler

10. "New York is not Mecca. It just smells like it." —Neil Simon

11. "A bookstore is one of the only pieces of evidence we have that people are still thinking." —Jerry Seinfeld

12. "I dream for a living." —Steven Spielberg

13. "A song is anything that can walk by itself." —Bob Dylan

14. "It is every woman's dream to be some man's dream woman." —Barbra Streisand

15. "I think of my body as a side effect of my mind." —Carrie Fisher

16. "Gentlemen, start your egos." —Billy Crystal

17. "If you don't risk anything, you risk even more." —Erica Jong

18. "Your dresses should be tight enough to show you're a woman and loose enough to show you're a lady." —Edith Head

19. "Hey, I may loathe myself, but it has nothing to do with the fact that I'm Jewish." —Larry David

20. "I'm Jewish, but I'm totally not." —Sarah Silverman

21. "Communism is like one big phone company." —Lenny Bruce

22. "A man is only as good as what he loves." —Saul Bellow

23. "Creationists make it sound as though a theory is something you dreamt up after being drunk all night." —Isaac Asimov

24. "From each according to his abilities, to each according to his needs." —Karl Marx

25. "You cannot simultaneously prevent and prepare for war." —Albert Einstein

26. "I should warn you: If I turn out to be particularly clear, you've probably misunderstood what I've said." —Alan Greenspan

27. "You can't put your feet on the ground until you've touched the sky." —Paul Auster

28. "Never go for the punch line. There might be something funnier on the way." —Jerry Stiller

29. "Everybody ought to have a Lower East Side in their life." —Irving Berlin

30. "Songs are life in 80 words or less." —Neil Diamond

31. "Misfits aren't misfits among other misfits."—Barry Manilow

32. "The Republicans are the party of bad ideas. The Democrats are the party of no ideas." —Lewis Black

33. "I've had great success being a total idiot." —Jerry Lewis

34. "It's easier to put on slippers than to carpet the whole world." —Al Franken

35. "Anatomy is destiny." —Sigmund Freud

36. "Both the man of science and the man of action live always at the edge of mystery, surrounded by it." —J. Robert Oppenheimer

37. "Einstein, stop telling God what to do!" —Niels Bohr

38. "Accent your positive and delete your negative." —Donna Karan

39. "Life is a lot like jazz…it's best when you improvise." —George Gershwin

40. "Google's not a real company." —Steve Ballmer

41. "Life improves slowly and goes wrong fast, and only catastrophe is clearly visible." —Edward Teller

42. "My strength is coming up with two outs in the last of the ninth." —Michael Eisner

43. "You can only work for people you like." —Milton Glaser

44. "Colorless green ideas sleep furiously." —Noam Chomsky

45. "Some men are born mediocre, some men achieve mediocrity, and some men have mediocrity thrust upon them." —Joseph Heller

46. "America, I've given you all, and now I'm nothing." —Allen Ginsberg

47. "I've never been a millionaire, but I know I'd be darling at it." —Dorothy Parker

48. "If you ever forget you're a Jew, a Gentile will remind you." —Bernard Malamud

49. "Alimony is the curse of the writing class." —Norman Mailer

50. "To be a Jew is a destiny." —Vicki Baum